Iri

IRISH LAKE DWELLING OF THE ISOLATED TYPE.
Ideally restored from inspection of numerous sites.

Translated and retold by

Richard Marsh

Legendary Books
Dublin

Legendary Books
Irish King and Hero Tales
ISBN 978-0-9557568-2-5

Published by

Richard Marsh
15 Fontenoy Street
Dublin 7, Ireland
Phone 353-1-8827941
www.RichardMarsh.ie
Richard@RichardMarsh.ie

Trade enquiries to Irish Book Distribution

Also by Richard Marsh:
Spanish and Basque Legends, Legendary Books, 2010
Tales of the Wicklow Hills, Legendary Books, 2007
The Legends and Lands of Ireland, Sterling, 2004

Front cover: the Punchestown Standing Stone near Naas, County Kildare. (See The Spear of Maelodrán and the Spear of Belach Durgein.)

Back cover: the Proleek Dolmen near Dundalk, County Louth, one of the 366 Beds of Diarmuid and Gráinne.

Title page: Crannóg from *The Lake Dwellings of Ireland* by W. G. Wood-Martin, 1886.

Water mill drawing page 82 and maps by Christine Warner. Lagore brooch engraving page 86 from Wood-Martin, *The Lake Dwellings of Ireland*. Fionn graphic page 137 © Simon Brooks.

Contents

Historical Legends

Fionn mac Cumhaill and the Fianna

3

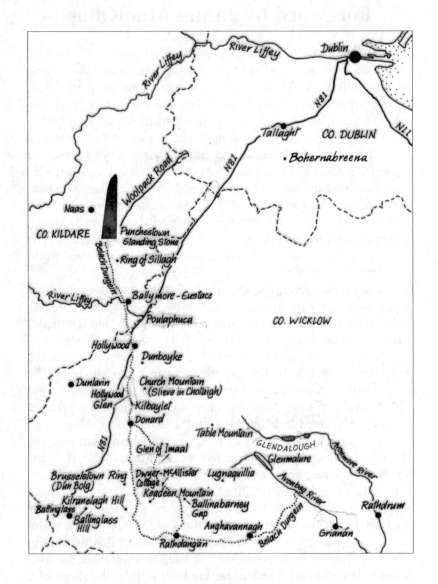

Places mentioned in the text
.... Proposed route(s) of Belach Durgein

Foreword by James MacKillop

As a tour guide, Richard Marsh has trod continually on Irish roads and boreens. Those well-spent hours explain the uniqueness of this collection. We see again and again that no matter how obscure, mysterious, fantastic or merely ancient a story is, he can root it in a specific place on the Irish map. Such geography – reality – is by no means incidental. The stories in this collection were recorded by privileged and learned scribes, who presumed informed readers and listeners. Their discourse was vastly different from that of shanachees who entertained illiterate peasants in later generations. The narratives of *Irish King and Hero Tales* were written when only a tiny prestigious minority could read. Marsh, however, aims to open the texts to a wide modern readership. His method signals reassurance. These stories, from a vanished world in a language few of us speak, can still be known.

For several centuries, the texts of these narratives were no longer read, in part because the English domination of Ireland reduced the number of people who could read Irish, and familiarity with the older language vanished. When that knowledge was recovered in the mid-nineteenth century, foreigners like the Englishman Whitley Stokes and the German Kuno Meyer led the way. Their translations, often retaining the complex phrasing and syntax of early Irish, were intended for a minuscule coterie of scholars, who cared little for the stories' entertainment value.

The resonant characterization of kings and heroes attracted the attention of hundreds of modern writers, starting with W. B. Yeats and James Joyce, and more recently of popular fantasy writers. This led to popularized retellings of the tales that smoothed away their strangeness and flattened their mystery. Bowing to accuracy, Richard Marsh favours the constructions of the best scholars. But like a welcome fellow-traveller helping the seeker find the way in strange terrain, he tells you what you need to know: that the Irish word *bruiden* (a hostel or banqueting hall) reflects the shape of a man's lips as he blows a fire.

James MacKillop is the author of *The Dictionary of Celtic Mythology* (Oxford) and *Myths & Legends of the Celts* (Penguin).

5

Introduction

Few people outside the academic world are familiar with or even aware of many of the fascinating historical legends preserved in medieval Irish manuscripts. The stories in this book are part of my storytelling repertoire – although my telling versions are much simplified – and I offer them here to a wider audience so that they might receive the attention they deserve. Parts of these written versions are my translations from the Irish and quotes from other translators, where I felt I could not improve on the original or the translation, and other parts are paraphrases or retellings, where my sources were too wordy, repetitive or obscure for modern tastes. Most of "Conaire the Great" and "The Champion's Portion" is fairly close translation, because I wanted to preserve the vibrant style and art of the original writers.

Apart from "Conaire the Great", which has only a tenuous hold on reality, and "The Champion's Portion", which is a rollicking burlesque of the hero tales, the stories in the Historical Legends section are based on historical fact and real people. Brief introductions to the stories place them in historical or legendary context. I have inserted some notes and explanations into the text when I thought they would not detract from the flow of the narrative, footnoted other relevant items and quote sources, and placed additional information not essential to the enjoyment of the story in the Notes section at the back of the book. The Bibliography includes sources of footnoted quotes.

According to a poem in the 12th-century *Book of Leinster*, 120 stories about Fionn mac Cumhaill and the Fianna were in the repertoires of the storytellers, and many of these stories are still told in homes and schools. Fionn has always been the hero of the ordinary people, unlike the elite warriors of the historical legends. Fionn and Cúchulainn were cousins, sharing the same great-grandfather, the Fomorian Balor of the Evil Eye.

The substance of "The Saga of Maelodrán" and "The Spear of Maelodrán and the Spear of Belach Durgein" was published in *Wicklow Archaeology and History*, Vol. 2, 2002, as "The Spear of Belach Durgein".

About the Author

Richard Marsh is a storyteller specialising in Irish, Spanish and Basque legends. He tells in Ireland and elsewhere and collects stories on his travels. In Ireland, he is also a Legendary Tour guide, taking people to the places where the legends happened and telling them on site.

Abbreviations

AFM – Annals of the Four Masters (in full: *Annals of the Kingdom of Ireland from the Earliest Times to the Year 1616*) – see O'Donovan, John.

DIL – *Dictionary of the Irish Language Based Mainly on Old and Middle Irish Materials*, Compact Edition, Royal Irish Academy, Dublin, 1983; on-line edition eDIL.

JKAS – *Journal of the Kildare Archaeological Society*.

JRSAI – *Journal of the Royal Society of Antiquaries of Ireland*.

MS Mat. – see O'Curry, Eugene, *Lectures on the Manuscript Materials ...*

PRIA – *Proceedings of the Royal Irish Academy*.

RC – *Revue Celtique*.

Historical Legends

The amount of history that is enshrined in these stories is still a matter for investigation. ... It seems to me likely, however, that the historians of the future will discover that Conn of the Hundred Battles and Eogan Mór and Cathaer Mór, king of Leinster, and the famous Cormac Mac Airt were historical persons, and that a fairly reliable historical tradition can be established from as early a time as the second century of the Christian era.

Myles Dillon, *The Cycles of the Kings*, 1946.

8

Conaire the Great

First written down about the eighth century and preserved in the 12th-century *Lebor na hUidre* (*The Book of the Dun Cow*) and later manuscripts, this story relates the downfall of Conaire Mór, a king of Ireland who died in 40 BC. Its Irish title is "Togail Bruidne Da Derga – The Destruction of Dá Derga's Hostel". Mythic elements abound, and most experts say that Conaire was not a real person but that the events are more or less historical. No one has explained why Conall Cernach and other Ulster heroes were imported into this Leinster saga, but the reason is probably that the Ulster Cycle of tales was prominent when the story was written. This part-retelling and part-translation, about one-third the length of the *Lebor na hUidre* version, deletes many repetitions and superfluous details.

The romantic mythological tale of Midir and Étaín serves as prologue to this story. The Sidhe (Otherworld) lord Midir abducted Étaín, the wife of the human high king Eochaid Airem, and Eochaid dug up several *sídh* (fairy) mounds to recover her. The Sidhe people would exact their revenge for this destruction by manipulating Eochaid's grandson, Conaire, into violating the *geasa* (singular: *geis*; magical or ritual prohibitions) imposed on him by his birdman father, thereby bringing about his death. (Combining academic and popular usage, I use "sídh" for the mound and "Sidhe" for the people of the mounds. Both are pronounced "shee".)

Eochaid's daughter, Mess Buachalla, was chosen by Eterscel, the next high king, to be his wife. Before their wedding, a birdman came to her, took off his bird skin, and lay with her. He told her she would give birth to his son, who was to be called Conaire, and he laid the *geis* on him that he was forbidden to kill birds. But she neglected to tell Conaire about this prohibition.

9

Conaire's three foster brothers were his nephews, sons of his sister and Donn Desa, Eterscel's champion: Fer Le, Fer Gair and Fer Rogain. Conaire had three gifts, hearing, far-seeing and judgement, and he gave one to each of his foster brothers.

When King Eterscel died, the foster brothers told Conaire he should go to the bull feast at Tara for the selection of the next king. In this ritual, a bull was slaughtered, and a seer drank its blood and ate its flesh, then wrapped himself in its still-steaming hide and slept. In a vision he would see the divinely appointed new king of Ireland. Three kings watched each of the four great roads to Tara until a man fitting the description came along.

Conaire set off for Tara alone, and on his way he saw speckled birds of unusual size and great beauty. He gave chase, but they remained a spear-cast ahead of him until he used his sling and overcame them. Then the birds took off their bird skins and one of them came to him and said, "I am Nemglan, your father and king of the bird realm. Don't you know that the birds are your cousins and you are forbidden to kill them?"

"I didn't know that until today," said Conaire.

"Last night," said Nemglan, "the bull-feaster saw in his vision a naked man with a sling and a stone walking along one of the roads to Tara. Go thus to Tara and be king."

And Nemglan laid eight more geasa on him.

He was not to pass Tara on his right hand or Bregia (the plain around Tara) on his left hand, not to hunt the "crooked beasts" (probably swans) of Cerna, not to stay away from Tara for nine consecutive nights, not to stay in a house from which firelight was visible and which could be seen into, not to allow three reds to precede him into the house of Red, not to allow plunder to be taken while he was king, not to allow the visit of a single woman or man into a house after sunset where he was staying, and not to settle a quarrel between two of his subjects unless they asked him to intervene.

So Conaire stripped off his clothes and walked towards Tara with his sling and a stone. He was soon sighted and taken to Tara for the final test. Untamed horses were yoked to a chariot, and Conaire drove them towards the two stones called Blocc and Bluigne, which then stood so close together a man could barely pass the blade of his hand between them. The stones moved apart to allow the chariot through. Then Conaire drove to the Lia Fáil (Stone of Destiny), which at that time stood in front of the passage tomb known as the Mound of the Hostages, and grazed it with the hub of his wheel so that it cried out in the voice of the local earth goddess. He was thus confirmed as the rightful king and began a reign that lasted seventy years.

During his reign, the mast (acorns as pig-feed) was knee-deep every autumn, there were plenty of fish in the rivers, no wind blew strong enough to disturb a cow's tail from spring to autumn, and such was the good will among the people that the sound of everyone's voice was sweet to their neighbour's ear and no one was slain.

This did not please Conaire's foster brothers, for they were accustomed to robbing and killing. They used to rob a certain man every year of a pig, a cow and an ox to see if they could get away with it. That man would go to Conaire to complain, and Conaire would tell him to sort out the problem himself with the foster brothers. Allowing this plundering violated one of Conaire's geasa. Thus encouraged, the sons of Donn Desa gathered three fifties of the sons of lords and set out to plunder Connacht. They were arrested and brought before Conaire.

"Each father may slay his own son if he wishes," he said, "but let my foster brothers be sent into exile."

The people agreed on exile for all, and the young men followed the sons of Donn Desa over the Irish Sea, where they joined Ingcél Cáech ("One-eyed"), son of the king of Britain, and his band of reavers, who were plundering Britain and Scotland. The reavers killed Ingcél's mother and father and seven brothers in the house of the king. Then the sons of Donn Desa invited the band to plunder Ireland.

There was peace in Ireland at this time, except for a dispute between two lords named Corpre in North Munster. Without being asked, Conaire went there, settled the quarrel, and spent five nights with each of the men (staying away from Tara for nine consecutive nights), thereby transgressing two more geasa. Meanwhile, Ingcél's marauders had arrived and were plundering the area around Tara. As Conaire drove back from Munster by way of

11

Uisnech, he could see the country in flames with smoke and naked refugees everywhere.

"What's happening here?" Conaire asked the people.

"The king's law has broken down and the country is burning," they answered.

"What way should we go?"

"Northeast."

And so Conaire drove right-hand round Tara and left-hand round Bregia, inadvertently hunting the crooked beasts of Cerna in the process and thus breaking two more geasa. He didn't realise what he was doing because the Sidhe people had conjured up a magic mist that blended with the smoke to confuse him. He drove south on the Slige Chualann, crossing the River Liffey and skirting the western side of the Dublin Mountains.

"Where shall we spend the night?" he asked his champion, Mac Cécht.

"It's more usual for the men of Ireland to be competing for the honour of your presence, than that you should be looking for a place to stay," said Mac Cécht.

"Fruit comes in season, and judgement in its time," said Conaire. "I have a friend who lives in this area, if only I knew where his house is."

"What's his name?"

"Dá Derga. He asked me for a gift once, and he didn't go away empty-handed. I gave him a hundred choice cattle, a hundred grass-fed swine, a hundred fine-woven mantles, and a hundred battle-weapons. I gave him ten red gilded brooches, ten vats of good drink, ten slaves, ten grain mills, three nines of white hounds with silver chains, and a hundred champion racehorses. It would be strange if he didn't offer us hospitality."

"I know Dá Derga's Hostel," said Mac Cécht. "The road we're on will take us there. In fact, the road goes right through the house. There are seven doorways, but only one door, which is used to block whichever doorway is facing the wind. I'll go ahead and light a fire in your room."

(The Hostel probably straddled the River Dodder where it runs through Bohernabreena – Road of the Hostel, from the Irish *bóthar na bruidne* – near Tallaght in southwest County Dublin,

12

where the present-day R411 makes two sharp turns to cross the river. The Irish word for hostel, *bruiden*, comes from the shape of a man's lips when he blows a fire, according to the *Lebor na hUidre* scribe.)

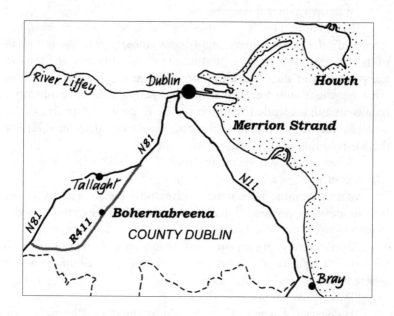

After Mac Cécht and most of the company had gone, Conaire saw three red-haired riders on red horses ahead of him wearing red shirts and mantles and carrying red shields and spears. Everything about them was red, even their teeth.

"Who is that ahead of us?" said Conaire. "It is a geis of mine for the three of them to go before me, three reds to the house of Red [Derga]. Who will go after them and tell them to pull up and fall in behind me?"

"I'll go after them," said Conaire's seven-year-old son, Lé Fri Flaith.

Lé Fri Flaith lashed his horse forward but was not able to overtake them. The riders maintained the length of a spear-cast in front of him. He shouted at them not to ride before the king. One of them sang over his shoulder:

"Bird Son, great news from the Hostel down the road.
A house of ashes, hanged man high-reeking, grief and
wounding, curses, butchery. Bé Find, the Pale Woman, sits
astride the blood-red pack of slaughter. Bird Son."

They galloped away from him and he was not able to keep up.
He waited for his father to arrive and told him what the man had
said.

"Go after them," said Conaire. "Offer them three oxen and
three pigs and tell them that in my house no one will come
between them and the fire."

The boy went after them but could not catch them, and one of
them sang over his shoulder:

"Bird Son, great news, it heats, it warms, a warning to
an open-handed king of fake generosity, a wise man
hindered by a heavy set of nine [geasa]. Bird Son."

Lé Fri Flaith reported this to his father, and Conaire said, "Go
after them and tell them six oxen and six pigs and whatever is left
over tomorrow, and in my house no one will come between them
and the fire."

The boy went after them but could not overtake them, and one
of them sang over his shoulder:

"Bird Son, great news, the weary steeds we ride are those of
Donn Tetscoraig of the Sidhe. Alive we are and not alive,
the banished ever-living. Vultures will be satisfied, ravens
fed, sword-edge whetting, alder-shields are shorn of bosses
after sunset. Bird Son."

When Conaire heard this, he said, "All my geasa have
overtaken me,"[1] for he knew that the three red riders were of the
immortal race banished by men to the mounds and under the earth,
now returned to this world to work their vengeance on him for his

---

[1] Not yet. Two more remain to be violated.

14

grandfather's deeds. The riders went on ahead to the Hostel, tied their steeds to the door and took their seats inside.

Then a man with one eye, one arm and one leg approached Conaire. His black hair was so spiky that if you threw a bushel of crab-apples on his head they would be impaled on the hairs, and not one would land on the ground. His nose was so big that if you flung it over a branch it would hang there. His shins were as long and thick as a yoke, and his buttocks were the size of two rounds of cheese. He carried a forked iron cooking spit in his hand and a black-charred, rough-bristled pig on his back that never ceased squealing. Behind him walked a fat, dark, hideous, miserable wide-mouthed woman, whose lower lip hung to her knees.

The man said, "Welcome, Lord Conaire, your coming has been long awaited."

"Who is giving me this welcome?" said Conaire.

"Fer Caille, with a pig for your dinner so that you won't have to go without food tonight, for you are the best king that has ever come into the world."

"What's your wife's name?"

"Cichuil."

"I'll come to you some other night when it's convenient for you," said Conaire, "but leave us alone tonight."

"No," said the man. "We're going to stay in the same place you stay tonight, dear Lord Conaire." And he continued on to the Hostel, with the squealing black-charred rough-bristled pig on his back and his fat, wide-mouthed wife behind him.

(The man's name, "Man of the Forest", and the woman's name, "Breasty", and her exaggerated description indicate that she is the *cailleach*, a goddess figure, who appears as here in the form of the *badhbh*[2] to those doomed to die. The *cailleach* is often associated with pigs, which originated in the Otherworld.)

Meanwhile, the reavers had arrived at Howth. Ingcél, huge, fearsome and uncouth, with one black three-pupiled eye as wide as an ox hide, led 1300 British bandits and an even greater number of Irish marauders. Fer Le, Fer Gair and Fer Rogain climbed the Hill of Howth, and with the gifts of hearing, far-seeing and judgement

---

[2] Rhymes with "hive" or "how", depending on region and era.

given to them by their foster brother Conaire, they spied Conaire and his retinue on the road. They reported back to Ingcél, and the outlaws' fleet of 150 boats and 5000 men set off across Dublin Bay and headed for Merrion Strand. Just as they were about to land, Mac Cécht was striking a spark to light the fire in the room Conaire was to occupy in the Hostel of Dá Derga. The sound of that striking hurled the boats back out to sea. Ingcél asked what it was, and Fer Rogain explained that it was the sound of Mac Cécht lighting a fire for the King of Ireland.

"Every spark and spray of flame from that man's fire that falls to the floor would cook a hundred calves and two half-pigs."

"God grant that Conaire doesn't come there tonight," said the sons of Donn Desa. "It would be a grievous thing for him to be attacked."

"No more grievous than the plundering I gave you in Britain," said Ingcél. "It would be a feast for me for Conaire to be there."

When Conaire and his retinue arrived at Dá Derga's Hostel, the three red riders of the Sidhe and Fer Caille with his pig were already seated inside. Dá Derga came in followed by three fifties of warriors with neck-length hair. They wore short green-speckled trousers and short capes and carried heavy blackthorn clubs with iron bands. Dá Derga greeted Conaire: "At your service, Master Conaire. If you had brought all the men of Ireland with you they would all be welcome."

The reavers' fleet landed on Merrion Strand, and the boats struck the shore with such an earth-shaking thump that the weapons on the walls of the Hostel cried out and fell to the floor.

"What was that sound?" everyone asked Conaire.

"If it's not the end of the world, it means that the Sons of Donn Desa have landed. Alas that it should be those champions, my beloved foster brothers, who threaten us tonight."

A woman wearing a striped fleecy cloak came to the door after sunset and asked to be let in. Her shins were as long as a weaver's beam and as dark as the back of a beetle. Her mouth was on the side of her head. She leaned against the doorpost and cast an evil eye on Conaire and his men.

"Well, woman," said Conaire. "What do you see, if you're a seer?"

"I see that neither hide nor flesh of yours will come out of this place, save what the birds can carry away in their claws."

"That's not the ill omen we were prophesied, woman," said Conaire. "You're not our usual soothsayer. What's your name?"

"Calib."

"That's not much of a name."

"I have other names."

"Which are?"

Standing on one foot with one hand raised in the stance of a poet pronouncing the dreaded Glam Dícenn curse, she chanted in one breath: "Samon Sinad Seisclend Sodb Saiglend Caill Coll Díchóem Díchiúil Díthim Díchuimne Dichruidne Dairne Dáríne Déruaine Égem Ágam Ethamne Gním Cluiche Cethardam Níth Némain Nóennen Badb Blosc Boár Huae Óe Aife la Sruth Mache Médé Mod."

"What have you come here for?" said Conaire.

"The same thing you've come for," said the woman. "Hospitality."

"It is geis for me to allow a solitary woman to come in after sunset."

"Geis or not," said she, "I won't leave until I've been accepted as a guest here tonight."

"Tell her," said Conaire, "that I'll have an ox and a pig and the leftovers from my plate sent out to her, if she agrees to stay in some other place."

The woman said, "If the king has so far lost his sense of hospitality that he has no meal or bed for a lone woman, I'll find food and accommodation elsewhere."

"A savage answer," said Conaire. "Let her in."

They all felt a horror and foreboding at this, and they did not know why. (This broke the last of the nine geasa, the eighth violation being caused by the "boar fire": not to stay in a house from which firelight was visible and which could be seen into.)

From their landing place at Merrion Strand the reavers could see the glow of the "boar fire" in the Hostel. This fire was built in a circle with seven gaps, and from each gap a flame burst forth that could consume an oratory.

"Fer Rogain," said Ingcél. "What is that glow in the sky?"

17

"It looks like the fire of the king, Conaire himself. God grant that he isn't there. It would be a terrible thing to destroy him."

"What sort of king is he?" said Ingcél.

"Since he became king no day has been without sun from spring to autumn, the dew stays on the grass till midday, and no breeze turns the hair of the hide of a cow till mid-afternoon. During his reign no wolf has attacked more than one calf of a herd in a year, and seven wolves are held hostage as surety. The three crops of Ireland have flourished during his reign: corn, flowers and acorns. The people find one another's voices as melodious as lute strings because of the excellence of his rule and the peace and benevolence that result. God grant that it is not Conaire who is there tonight, for it would be a pity to slaughter him, to shorten his life."

"Fortunate for me," said Ingcél, "that he should be here, so that there will be one destruction for another. It is no more distressing to me than the killing I gave you of my mother and father, the king of my people, and my seven brothers."

"That's true," agreed the hard men among the band.

The reavers started off from Merrion Strand and each brought with him a stone to make a cairn, for it was the custom of warrior bands to erect a pillar stone to commemorate a Rout, and a cairn to mark a Destruction. After they had passed Oe Cualann (Sugarloaf Mountain), but still at some distance from the Hostel, where they could not be seen or heard, they built a cairn, for this was to be a Destruction. They raised the cairn so that they could calculate their losses: whoever did not return from the attack would not remove his stone from the cairn, and so the stones that make up Carn Leca in Cualu Uí Cheallaig (southwest County Dublin, northwest Wicklow) reveal the number of marauders slain at the Hostel.

The sons of Donn Desa kindled a "boar fire" to warn Conaire. That was the first warning beacon in Ireland, and from it has every warning fire been lit to this day. Some say that the destruction of the Hostel occurred on Samhain Eve – the eve of the first of November – and from that fire come the Samhain Eve fires of today.

"Now, what place is nearest to us?" Ingcél asked the sons of Donn Desa.

18

"The Hostel of Dá Derga, the chief guesthouse keeper in Ireland."

"Good," said Ingcél. "There should be a crowd of people gathered there tonight. I'll go and spy out the house, because I have the strongest claim."

Ingcél went and reconnoitred the Hostel with the three pupils of the one eye that stood out of his forehead, for he could see into the house through the wheels of the seventeen chariots that were ranged outside the doors. (This confirms the breaking of the eighth geis.) He was seen from the Hostel, and he returned to the reavers to report: "Whatever it is, it's a royal gathering. Whether a king is there or not, I'll take the house as my due."

"It would be our foster brother, Conaire Mór son of Eterscel, High King of Ireland, who is there. Who did you see in the champion's seat opposite the King?"

"A large man with a noble, just, beardless face broad above and narrow below, with clear eyes and an even set of teeth. He wears a fine cloak with a silver brooch. In one hand he holds a gold-hilted sword, and in the other a five-pronged javelin and a shield with five gold concentric circles. A modest-minded man."

"That's Cormac Cond Longas son of Conor," said Fer Rogain, "the best man behind a shield in Ireland. I swear by the gods my people swear by, nine tens will fall by him in his first strike, and nine tens will fall by his people, and a man for each of their weapons, and a man for each of themselves. Cormac himself will win victory over a king or a prince or a noble of the reavers and then escape, though all his people will be wounded."

"Alas for him who wreaks this destruction," said Lomna Drúth, another son of Donn Desa. "This destruction should not be attempted, if only for that one man."

"It can't be stopped now, Lomna," said Ingcél. "Your voice is breaking. Clouds of weakness have come over you. You are a worthless warrior."

"It's hard for me," said Lomna Drúth. "It's my head that will be the first to be tossed about there tonight. It will be flung into the Hostel and out again three times."

19

Ingcél then described and Fer Rogain identified all who were in the Hostel, followed by Lomna's misgivings and Ingcél's abuse of Lomna.

Cormac Cond Longas's nine identical companions wearing gold-striped cloaks carried ivory-hilted swords, curved bronze shields and ridged spears. They performed a unique feat: each took the point of his sword between his two fingers and twirled the sword around his fingers, and then the sword lengthened by itself.

Three enormous brown exiled Picts attached to Conaire's household, who will kill nine tens in the first assault. Their hair was equally long front and back on their round heads, covered with black cowls to their elbows. They carried huge black swords, black-studded shields and broad blue thick-shafted javelins.

Nine golden-haired Otherworld pipers that Conaire had brought out of Sídh Breg, the best pipers in the world and all equally beautiful. The ornament on their bagpipes could light up the whole palace. Fighting with them will be like fighting with shadows: they will slay nine tens and a king or chief of the reavers, but they will not be slain, for they are of the Sidhe.

Conaire's champion, Mac Cécht, so gigantic that his eyes looked like lakes, his nose like a mountain, his knees like hills, his shoes like boats. He had a 30-foot sword that shot out sparks and a spear with a four-foot wide iron-tipped blade. When he shook the spear it would bend so that the ends touched. His wooden shield could hold four troops of ten men each, and the boss in the centre of it was like a cauldron, deep and wide enough to contain four oxen and four pigs. When he attacks, heads and brains and bones and intestines will fly in the air like hailstones. He will kill 600 in his first onslaught. Ingcél admitted that he nearly fainted with horror when he saw him, and his description caused the other reavers to flee three ridges away so that they had to be re-assembled and made to pledge themselves again for the venture.

"Who else did you see?" Fer Rogain asked Ingcél.

"Three young boys with long fleecy golden-yellow hair that hangs to their haunches when it is washed, but reaches no lower than the tips of their ears when they raise their eyes. Who are they, Fer Rogain?"

20

When Fer Rogain heard that, he wept so much that his cloak was wetted, and there was no voice from his head for a third of the night.

"Oh, little ones," he finally said, "I have to do what I am going to do. They are three sons of the King of Ireland, Oball and Oblíne and Corpre Findmor. They have the hearts of brothers and the courage of bears and the fury of lions. Three tens will fall by each of them, and one will be slain."

"What else did you see?" they asked Ingcél, and he continued to describe and Fer Rogain to identify the others.

Three Fomorian hostages brought out of the land of the Fomorians by Mac Cécht. They were held as surety that the Fomorians would not ravage the crops of Ireland while Conaire was king. They had three rows of teeth in their mouths and ate an ox and a pig every day. They had no weapons because they were hostages, but they will kill 600 in the first attack with bites and blows and kicks. If they had weapons they would kill a third of the reavers.

Three princes, Munremar, Birderg and Mál, whose limbs were as thick as a man's waist, dressed in red and speckled cloaks. They threw their ivory-hilted swords up in the air and the scabbards after them, and the swords inserted themselves into the scabbards before reaching the ground. Then they threw the scabbards up and after them the swords, and the scabbards wrapped themselves around the swords before they reached the ground. A hundred heroes will fall by them in the first clash.

Conall Cernach in a purple cloak, the greatest of the Ulster heroes (Cúchulainn was not born yet), with his one hyacinth-blue eye and one beetle-black eye, one cheek white as snow and the other red and speckled like a foxglove. His bushy golden hair fell to his waist. A gold-hilted sword was in his hand. *Bricriu* (Bitter-tongue) is the name the Ulstermen gave to Conall's shield, blood-red with white-gold rivets between gold plates. His three-ridged spear was long and heavy and as thick as a yoke, and it will serve many a red drink tonight at the door of the Hostel. He will manage to be at each of the seven doorways at once, and 300 will fall at his first attack.

21

A beautiful youth with the force and impetuous energy of a hero and the wisdom of a sage lay asleep. He awoke and chanted: "The howl of Conaire's dog, Ossar, a warrior-shout on the peak of Tol Gossi, a cold wind over perilous blades, a night for the taking of a king is this night." He slept and woke again and chanted: "Battle, sack of the Hostel, warriors wounded, wind of terror, feast of weapons, Tara desolate, downfall of the King of Ireland, lament for Conaire." He slept again and woke and chanted: "I saw strife, a host laid low, foes overthrown, a fray on the Dodder, Ossar's howl." As the proverb runs, "There is no conflict without a king." This was Conaire himself, unchanged in appearance through his seventy years in the kingship. Six hundred will fall by him before he is able to take up his weapons, and 600 more in his first onrush after he arms himself.

There was a freckle-faced boy with green, auburn and golden hair wearing a purple cloak: Conaire's seven-year-old son, Lé Fri Flaith, who wept continually for the evil he dreaded this night. The fifteen men who went with Ingcél to spy out the Hostel were all blinded in the right eye by the sight of him, and Ingcél himself lost the sight in one of the three pupils in his one eye.

Fer Rogain explained the presence of the three Red men from the sídh-mounds. They had committed falsehood in the Otherworld. Their punishment was to be destroyed by three kings of Tara, and they had come to this world to be destroyed for the last time by Conaire. But they will not be slain, nor will they slay anyone.

As the reavers approached the Hostel, the bald juggler Tulchinne was juggling nine swords, nine silver shields and nine golden apples. He threw them all up in the air, and only one was in his palm at a time as they rose and fell in the air like bees on a warm day. Suddenly, just when Tulchinne was juggling at his swiftest, all the objects clattered to the ground, and his audience let out a cry.

Conaire said, "That is the first time I have ever seen you fail."

"Alas, good master Conaire, it's for a good reason. I felt the hostile gaze of a three-pupiled eye on me. Someone is watching from outside. Evil is at the door of the Hostel tonight. Donn Desa's sons have come to annihilate Conaire."

Ingcél gathered the marauders and said, "On, warriors, to the Hostel."

The sound of their approach came to Conaire's ears.

"Quiet," said Conaire. "What's that noise?"

"Warriors at the house," said Conall Cernach.

"We have heroes to meet them," said Conaire.

"They will be needed tonight."

Lomna Drúth marched to the Hostel at the head of the host. The doorkeeper cut off his head, and it was tossed three times into and out of the Hostel, as Lomna had foretold. Before he could arm himself, Conaire sallied forth and killed 600, then donned his battle-dress and took up arms and killed 600 more. Three times the Hostel was set on fire and three times the fire was put out.

The attack was repulsed, but the druids of the reavers wove a spell that put a great thirst on Conaire. It was discovered that all the water from the River Dodder, which flowed through the Hostel, had been used to extinguish the fires. Conaire asked his champion, Mac Cécht, to find water for him.

"I can either bring water or protect your body from spears," said Mac Cécht. "But I can't do both."

"It's the same to me whether I die of thirst or spear-wounding," said Conaire.

"Leave the defence of the king to us," Conall Cernach told Mac Cécht. "Go and get water as you were asked." This caused lasting bitterness between them.

So Mac Cécht took Conaire's son Lé Fri Flaith under his arm, and Conaire's golden cup, along with his own shield and spears and an iron cooking spit, and made a sally. He killed 600 with the iron spit and an edge-feat of the sword over his head and a sloping-feat with his shield, and set off in search of water.

Conall Cernach made a turn around the house and killed 300, though he was wounded, and he and the other heroes drove the reavers back the distance of three ridges. Then all fled the Hostel except Conall and the Ulster heroes Sencha and Dubtach, who remained with Conaire until he died of thirst, and then the warriors fought their way through the reavers and escaped.

Meanwhile, Mac Cécht had found all the lakes and rivers dried up by the enchantments of the druids, until he came to the

23

well of Uaran Garad in Magh Aí in Roscommon, which could not hide from him. Mac Cécht filled Conaire's cup from the well and brought it back to the Hostel.

As he reached the third ridge from the house he saw two men cutting off the head of Conaire. Mac Cécht struck the head off one of them. As the other was making off with Conaire's head, Mac Cécht hurled a pillar stone at him, breaking his back, and then beheaded him. Mac Cécht poured water into the king's neck, and Conaire's head spoke: "Good man, Mac Cécht, to give a king a drink. A gift for you, were I alive."

Mac Cécht pursued the reavers and killed all but Ingcél and four others, who escaped. (Ingcél returned to Scotland and became king.) Mac Cécht fell down exhausted from his wounds. A woman was passing by, and he hailed her.

"Come here, woman, and see what's in this wound. I don't know whether it's a fly or a midge or an ant that's nibbling me."

She saw that it was in fact a huge hairy wolf that was in the wound up to its shoulders. She grabbed the wolf by the tail and dragged it out of the wound, and it brought the full of its jaws with it.

"It was an ant of the old land," she said.

Mac Cécht took the wolf by the throat and killed it with a blow to the forehead. It was now that Lé Fri Flaith died. Having been carried all this time by Mac Cécht, he had melted in the heat and sweat of the warrior's armpit. Then Mac Cécht took Conaire's head and body to Tara and buried them there.

Conall Cernach arrived at his father, Amairgin's, house at Tailtiu with his sword, fragments of his two spears, and the remaining half of his shield. Three fifties of spears had gone through his shield arm.

"Swift the wolves that have hunted you, my son," said his father.

"It was a battle with seasoned warriors that did this, old hero," said Conall.

"What's the news from Dá Derga's Hostel?" said Amairgin. "Is your king alive?"

"He is not alive," said Conall.

"I swear by the gods that the great tribes of Ulster swear by, it's a poor warrior who leaves a battle alive while his lord lies dead among his enemies."

"My wounds are not white, old hero," replied Conall.

He showed Amairgin his left arm with only three fifties of wounds because it had been covered by the shield. Then he showed him his unprotected right arm, which was so pierced and hacked and riddled it only hung on his body by the sinews.

"That arm fought tonight, my son," said Amairgin.

"That it did, old hero. There are many who got a drink of death from it at the door of the Hostel tonight."

The Champion's Portion

This burlesque hero tale, usually called Fled Bricrend (The Feast of Bricriu), is set about 2000 years ago. The earliest known written version dates to the eighth century and was transcribed into surviving manuscripts between the 12th and the 16th century. My translation is based on the 12th-century *Lebor na hUidre* (*The Book of the Dun Cow*) and the 14-15th-century Edinburgh Gaelic MS XL, which is the only source of the ending of the story.

The main characters:

Cúchulainn, the greatest of the Ulster warriors, is the hero of the Irish epic, *Táin Bó Cuailnge*, The Cattle Raid of Cooley.

Loegaire Buadach (Victorious) is best known for his death-tale. King Conor discovered that his poet, Aed, was having an affair with his wife and condemned him to death, but allowed him to choose the method of execution. Aed chose drowning, because he had a spell that could dry up water. The spell worked on several lakes and rivers but failed with Loch Lai, in front of Loegaire's house. When Loegaire heard Aed's cry for help, he rushed out with his sword, striking his head on the lintel of the doorway and shearing off the back of his head so that his brains were splattered over his cloak. Nevertheless, he managed to kill thirty of the would-be executioners before he died, allowing the poet to escape.

Conall Cernach (Triumphant), foster brother of Cúchulainn and his lifelong friend (and sometimes rival), was the leader of the Red Branch warriors on an expedition to Britain to aid fellow Celts fighting against the Romans. He was captured and taken to Rome as a trophy, befriended by the Romans and given a tour of their provinces, arriving in the Holy Land at the time of the Crucifixion. There is a tradition that every nation of the world was present at the Crucifixion, and Conall was the Irish representative. He may have been a real person. His name appears in the family trees of later historical figures, including Saint Brigit and the 7th-century poet Ultan McConnel Cearnach.

Conor mac Nessa supplanted Fergus mac Róich as King of Ulster. Fergus wanted to marry Nessa. She agreed on condition that he allow Conor to be king for a year so that his sons could boast that they were sons of a king. Conor and Nessa bribed the nobles of Ulster with the result that at the end of the year they decided to keep Conor as king. Fergus became advisor to the Boy Troop.

Conor was reckoned by medieval theologians to be the first Christian in Ireland through the "red baptism" of martyrdom. Conor had survived an assassination attempt, but the weapon, a brain-ball made from the calcified brain of a slain warrior, remained lodged in his head. The doctors said that he would die if they removed it, and they warned that any exertion might expel the brain-ball and kill him. When Conall Cernach returned from the Holy Land and reported on the Crucifixion, Conor was so angry that a man of peace had been executed as a common criminal that he attacked trees with his sword. The exertion made the brain-ball pop out, and he died a martyr for his belief in Christ.

Sencha mac Ailella was poet, judge, historian and advisor to Conor.

Bricriu was a trouble-maker whose only pleasure in life was instigating quarrels so that people would fight and kill each other. He was trampled to death by the two bulls at the end of the *Táin*.

Queen Maeve of Connacht was once married to Conor, who divorced her, and she held a grudge against him. Her husband, Ailill, was not king, though he is referred to as such in this story. Connacht and Ulster were traditional enemies, which is why Ailill is suspicious of Conor's motive in choosing him as the arbiter in the dispute over the champion's portion. Cruachan Aí, near Tulsk, County Roscommon, was Maeve's royal seat.

Emer is one of the few positive strong female characters in early Irish literature. She is intelligent, clever and assertive, as shown here and in the stories of Cúchulainn's wooing of her, Tochmarc Emire, and her dispute with one of Cúchulainn's lovers, Fand, best known through Yeats's play *The Only Jealousy of Emer*. A native of Lusk, County Dublin, she compares herself with the Ulsterwomen, not the *other* Ulsterwomen.

Cú Roí mac Dáire was a powerful wizard-king living in County Kerry. Cúchulainn later seduced Cú Roí's wife, Bláthnat, and killed him. The remains of his fort, Caherconree, can be seen in the Slieve Mish Mountains west of Tralee.

Bricriu's Feast

Bricriu of the Poison Tongue arranged a feast for Conor mac Nessa, King of Ulster, and all the Ulstermen. A full year he spent organising the event. He built a magnificent house at his seat at Dún Rúdraige[3] in preparation for the dining and drinking of the feast and ordered it to be constructed after the style of the Red Branch Hall[4] at Emain Macha.[5] However, such were the elegance and beauty of the materials and design, the lustre and ornamentation of the pillars and facade, and the costliness and splendour of the entrance and portico, that Bricriu's banquet hall surpassed all others of the time.

The seating arrangement was modelled on that of the Banquet Hall at Tara. The interior measured some 30 feet from the central fire to the walls. It contained nine cubicles furnished with couches, the heads of which were fashioned of gold-plated bronze. Twelve couches were provided for the twelve leading warriors of Ulster. Bricriu ordered a royal couch for Conor installed at the head of the palace. It was raised above the other compartments and embossed with gold and silver and adorned with carbuncles and other precious stones that shone so bright as to make night seem like day. The quality of the workmanship matched the materials. Each cross-beam required a plough team to haul it, and it took a crew of seven mighty Ulstermen to install each house-pole. Thirty of the principal artisans of Ireland supervised the construction and fitting.

On the south side, Bricriu built a sun parlour as high as Conor's and the warriors' couches. He built and designed it for a

---

[3] Near Dundrum, County Down.
[4] The headquarters of the Ulster warriors, next to the royal palace at Emain Macha.
[5] The Ulster royal seat, near Armagh City, now known as Navan Fort.

particular reason. It had glass windows on all sides and one just for himself so that he could look down into the great hall from his own couch, because he knew that the Ulstermen would not allow him inside. When the hall and the sun parlour were completed, Bricriu furnished both with plaids and bedclothes, featherbeds and cushions, and put in a full supply of drink and food, so that nothing would be lacking in the way of material comfort. Then he went to Emain Macha to meet with Conor and the nobles of Ulster. They happened to be in assembly at Emain that day. After being welcomed, Bricriu sat beside Conor and addressed the Ulstermen:

"Come join me in a feast."

"It's all right with me," said Conor, "if it's all right with the Ulstermen."

Fergus mac Róich replied and the Ulster nobles agreed:

"We won't come, because our dead will number greater than our living after Bricriu stirs up strife amongst us if we come to the feast."

"It will be worse for ye, truly," said Bricriu, "what I will do if ye don't come."

"What exactly will you do if we don't?" said Conor.

"Indeed," said Bricriu, "I shall set king against king, chieftain against chieftain, hero against hero, and lord against lord until they kill one another, unless ye join me in the celebration of my feast."

"We wouldn't give you the satisfaction," said Conor.

"I'll set father against son so that they kill each other. If that doesn't succeed," he continued, "I'll incite mother against daughter. If that doesn't work, I'll raise such a dispute between the two breasts of every Ulsterwoman that they will beat each other until they are nothing but two putrid lumps."

"We'd better go," said Fergus, "or that will happen."

"Perhaps we should discuss this with the leading lights of Ulster," said Sencha mac Ailella.

"Evil will come of it," said Conor, "if we don't seek advice."

So all the nobles of Ulster held a conference, and Sencha advised them: "Since ye are forced to accept Bricriu's invitation, take sureties from him and surround him with eight swordsmen to make him leave the hall once the feast is served."

Conor's son, Furbaide Fer Bend, went to Bricriu and announced their decision.

"That's fine with me," said Bricriu. "It shall be so."

The Ulstermen set out from Emain Macha, each band with their king, each company with their under-king, each troop with their chieftain. Splendid and marvellous was the march that brought the mighty men and gallant heroes to the palace. Meanwhile, Bricriu was debating in his mind how best to sow discord among the Ulstermen in such a way that heads would be cut off in spite of the sureties. When all was clear in his mind after pondering and deliberating, he went to curry favour with Loegaire Buadach mac Connaid mac Ilíach.

"Well met, indeed, Loegaire Buadach," he said; "you stout striker of Bregia, doom-dealer of Meath, blazing bear, choicest of the Ulster warriors. Why are you not always awarded the champion's portion of Emain?"

"If I wanted it," he said, "I could have it."

"I can make you king of the warriors of Ireland," said Bricriu, "if you follow my advice."

"You're mocking me," said Loegaire.

"If you get the champion's portion in my house, you will have the champion's portion of Emain forever. It is proper that there be contention for the champion's portion of my house," said Bricriu, "for it is not the champion's portion of a fool's house.

"There is a vat of fine wine in the hall, large enough to hold three Ulster warriors. There is a seven-year-old boar that from the time he was a piglet you would see nothing in his mouth but porridge of new milk and gruel in spring and cream, fresh milk, nuts and cream in autumn, and meat and broth in winter. There is a pillar of a black bull, fully seven years old, that since he was a small calf you wouldn't see heather or furze in his mouth, only fresh milk, herbs, green grass and corn. A hundred loaves of wheaten bread baked with honey are provided in twenty-five baskets, four loaves in each. That's what the champion's portion in my house consists of," said Bricriu.

"As the foremost hero of Ulster, you are the most deserving of it, and it should go to you. As the guests applaud when the feast is served at the end of the day, let your charioteer stand up, and the champion's portion will be given to him."

"There will be dead men if that is not done," said Loegaire.

Bricriu laughed at that and was happy in his mind.

Now that he had Loegaire stirred up, he went to the band led by Conall Cernach.

"Well met, Conall," he said. "You are a warrior of victorious exploits, a greatness of trophies far beyond the rest of the Ulster warriors. Whenever the Ulstermen carry off a raid into foreign parts, you are three days and three nights ahead of them crossing ford after ford. Then again you provide rearguard protection on their return so that no enemy reaches you or goes through or around you. Why, then, are you never awarded the champion's portion?"

Although he had spent a good deal of time working the deception on Loegaire, he spent twice as much with Conall Cernach. Now that he had set Conall against Loegaire like a fine fool, Bricriu took himself off to the company led by Cúchulainn.

"Well met, Cúchulainn," he said: "O battle-victorious of Bregia, bright-mantled one of the Liffey Plain, darling of Emain, beloved of women and maidens. 'Hound of Cullan' is not a mere nickname of the day, for you are the glory of the Ulstermen. You protect them from attacks and conflicts, you seek justice for each one of them, you succeed where all others fail. All the men of Ireland submit to your weapons and noble deeds. Why, then, do you allow the champion's portion to go to all the other Ulstermen, when not one man in Ireland is capable of contending with you for it?"

"I swear by the oath my people swear by," said Cúchulainn: "he will be a man without a head, the man who comes forward to challenge me for it."

Bricriu parted from him then and went to join the throng as though he hadn't been promoting any discord at all. They arrived at Bricriu's house and took their assigned compartments in the banquet hall: king and prince, chiefs, sub-chieftains and attendants. One side of the hall was for Conor and the champions of Ulster, and the other side for Conor's wife, Mugain daughter of Echach

31

Fedlig, and her ladies-in-waiting. Those with Conor in the upper part of the hall were:

Fergus mac Róich
Feradach Find Fectnach
Celtchar mac Uthechair
Fedelmid Chilair Chétaig
Eogan mac Durthacht
Furbaide Fer Bend and Conor's two sons Fiacha and Fiachaig
Rochad mac Fathemon
Loegaire Buadach
Conall Cernach
Cúchulainn
Fergna mac Findchoíme
Fergus mac Leti
Cúscraid Mend Macha son of Conor
Connad mac Mornai
Erc mac Fedelmthe
Sencha mac Ailella
Illand son of Fergus
Three sons of Fiachach: Rus and Dáre and Imchad
Fintan mac Neill
Ceternd mac Fintain
Muinremur mac Geirrgind
Factna mac Sencada
Errge Echbél
Conla Sáeb
Amairgin mac Ecit (Conall Cernach's father)
Ailill Miltenga
Mend mac Salchadae
Dubtach Dóel Ulad (Chafer-tongue)
and Bricriu himself.

Also present were the cream of the Ulster warriors and their attendants and craftsmen. Then the performers played music and other entertainments until the feast was served. As soon as Bricriu set out the feast with all the side dishes, it was announced to him that he had to leave according to the surety given by his guarantors. The guarantors stood up then with their naked swords in their hands to drive him out of the house. Bricriu left the house with his retainers and made his way toward his sun parlour. As he reached the doorway of the banquet hall, he spoke: "The way the champion's portion has been prepared," he said, "is not the champion's portion of a foolish house. It should go to the most accomplished warrior among ye Ulstermen."

With that, he left, and the butler rose to divide the food. Loegaire Buadach's charioteer, Sedlang mac Ríangabra, also stood up and said to the butler: "Serve up that champion's portion to Loegaire Buadach, for he has a greater claim to it than the rest of the Ulster warriors."

Id mac Ríangabra, Conall Cernach's charioteer, rose and said the same thing about Conall. Then Láeg mac Ríangabra, Cúchulainn's charioteer, stood up and said:

"Give it out to Cúchulainn. It would be no disgrace on the other Ulstermen for it to be given to him, for he is the finest warrior amongst ye."

"That's not true," said Conall Cernach and Loegaire Buadach.

All three leapt up in the centre of the house and strapped on their shields and grabbed their swords. They attacked one another, and it seemed as if one side of the house was sky-high with flames – like Dinn Ríg – with the clash of swords and javelin-blades, and that the bright battle-goddess was on the other side with the whitening of shields. The clash of weapons shook the banquet hall and threw the other warriors into a panic. Conor and Fergus grew angry at seeing this intolerable behaviour and injustice – two men, Conall Cernach and Loegaire Buadach, attacking Cúchulainn. None of the Ulstermen dared intervene until Sencha spoke to Conor.

"Separate the men," he said.

Conor and Fergus went between them and forced their hands down to their sides.

"Carry out my request," said Sencha.

"We will," they said.

"This is my strong request," said Sencha: "that the champion's portion be divided among the whole company tonight.

And then submit it to the judgement of Ailill mac Mágach, for it will be impossible for the Ulstermen to settle this dispute without a determination from Cruachan Aí."

So food and drink were dispensed to them, and they gathered round the fire and got drunk and were content. Bricriu and his lady were in the sun parlour. From the position of his couch, he could see the situation in the banquet hall and how things were going there. He plotted how to stir up contention among the women as he had done with the men. Just as he started to work out how to do it, as if intention made it happen, Bricriu saw Fedelm Noíchride and her fifty women come out of the banquet hall after heavy drinking and pass by him.

"Good evening, wife of Loegaire Buadach," he said. "'Fedelm Noíchride – Honoured, Nine Times Beautiful' – is not merely a nickname for the superiority of your appearance, your intelligence and your ancestry: your father Conor, king of a province of Ireland, your husband Loegaire Buadach. I should not think it too great an honour that none of the women of Ulster should precede you into the banquet hall, so that all the womenfolk of Ulster would be, as it were, in attendance on you. Come you back first into the house tonight, and you will be queen over all the Ulsterwomen forever."

Fedelm set out with her fifty ladies to go three fields away from the house to a certain small field used as a toilet.

Then Lendabair daughter of Eogan mac Durthacht, Conall Cernach's wife, came out. Bricriu spoke to her:

"Greetings, Lendabair," he said. "'Lendabair' is not merely your nickname, for you are the darling and the desire of men all over the world for your splendour and nobility. As far as your husband outstrips the warriors of the world in skill at arms, so does your beauty surpass that of the women of Ulster."

However great the deception he worked on Fedelm, he worked twice as much on Lendabair in the same manner. Then Emer came out with her fifty women.

"I wish you well, Emer daughter of Forgaill Manach," said Bricriu: "wife of the finest man in Ireland. 'Emer Foltchaín' – Emer of the Fair Hair – is not merely your nickname, for you are the talk of the kings and sons of kings all over Ireland. As the sun

34

rules the height of heaven, so do you dominate all the women of the world for your shape and beauty and ancestry, for your youth and splendour and eminence, for your glory and discernment and eloquence."

However great the deception he worked on the other two women, he worked three times as much on Emer. So the three parties of women set off and came three fields distant from the house, and none of them realised that Bricriu had turned them against one another.

Soon they returned to the banquet hall, marching at a firm, fine, sedate pace across the first field with none of them more than a step ahead of the others. The second field was smooth and level, and their pace quickened accordingly. The next field was nearest the house, so each woman forged ahead of the other wives in apprehension. Each lifted her tunic up to her buttocks in an attempt to arrive first at the house, for what Bricriu had told each one in succession was that she who reached the house first would be queen of the whole kingdom.

The thundering of the wives, each with her fifty attendants, charging to be first to reach the house was as loud as the sound of fifty chariots attacking, and it made the house shake. The warriors inside nearly killed each other leaping to their weapons.

"Stop," said Sencha. "That's not enemies attacking, but Bricriu caused dissension among the women when they went out. I swear by the oath my people swear by," he said, "unless the house is closed against them there will be more dead in it than living."

The doorkeepers closed the door. Emer reached the house ahead of the other women because of her speed, and she leaned against the door and called out to the doorkeepers before the other women arrived. Loegaire Buadach, Conall Cernach and Cúchulainn sprang up, each wanting to open the door for his wife so that she would be the first to enter the house.

"There's going to be trouble tonight," said Conor.

He had a silver mace in his hand, and he struck it against the bronze leg of his couch to make the company take their seats.

"Stop," said Sencha. "There will be no fighting with swords here. Instead, let there be a battle of words."

Each woman was put under her husband's protection, and then began –

The Ulsterwomen's War of Words

Fedelm of the Nine Beauties, daughter of Conor, wife of Loegaire Buadach, was the first to speak:

"I was born of a noble womb,
eldest of my family and rank,
sprung from the body of a king as befits a queen,
restrained and dignified by nature.
I am said to be blessed with beauty and pleasing of figure.
I am praised for the fairness of my form,
raised in warrior ways,
favoured by birth to be the Brown Mouse[6] of red-hand Loegaire,
who defends the territory of Ulster,
strikes aggressively with strength equal to that of all the rest of the Ulster warriors.
He protects them, fights for them, avenges them –
the most famous of warriors, Loegaire
whose full complement of victories will surpass those of any other warrior.
Why should it not be Fedelm Fair Beauty,
full-gifted of form, warrior's snapping hound,
who is exalted above all other women in the convivial banquet hall?"

Next to speak was Lendabair, daughter of Eogan mac Durthacht, wife of Conall Cernach mac Amairgin:

"Because I am the picture of reason and poise,
grace of gait, fairness of form, flame-haired

---

[6] This is an allusion to a ferocious dog that devastated Ulster until it was killed by Celtchar mac Uthechair, one of those present at Bricriu's feast.

before the women of Ulster
in the royal banquet hall;
because my dear husband is
mighty conquering Conall,
strong-stepping, height of hope,
foremost in battle, second to none;
prizes he brings back to me of victories, of limed heads
from hard Ulster conflicts
he offers his shield to hold every ford,
he clears fords, he fights their combats,
he attends to a hero wanting a gravestone;
the driving son of Amairgin dares to dicker;
for Conall it is who fares far above other heroes
in fullness of feats.
Why should it not be Lendabair of the Lustrous Eyes
who is placed above all other women in the royal hall?"

Then Emer daughter of Forgaill Manach, wife of Cúchulainn,
spoke:

"All these qualities I possess:
gait, shape, intelligence, bearing, vigour, achievements,
glories.
Every fine form is judged by comparison to my noble
eye set in my fair face.
There is not found form or adornment or bearing,
there is not found wisdom or honour or purity,
there is not found power of noble love or intelligence
except in me.
It is for me that all the Ulstermen sigh.
I am the utter darling of their hearts.
Were I wild and wanton with them,
not one of their wives could hold her husband from one
day to the next.
Cúchulainn is my husband. He is not a basket dog.
A drop of blood on his spear,
froth of blood upon his sword,
glorious his body darkened with gore,

37

wounds on his limbs, more about his torso,
wondrous wild his eye sinking into his head, fine the
frenzy:
the ridge of his jutting jaw,
fiery red his eyes,
deep red his chariot wheels,
bloodstained his chariot rugs.
Bursting from the form of a horse to that of a breathing
man,
he salmon-leaps and shifts his shape again.
He does a noble feat, a blind feat, a hero feat,
strikes a single drop of water,
performs the nine-fold feat,
wages bloody battles,
lays low the world's proud armies and wreaks
destruction on them.
He is a man who shrinks from lying down, though
bloodstained from felling foes.
The other Ulstermen are like women prostrate in
childbirth.
My husband, Cúchulainn, is pure and noble of blood,
unlike the other Ulster warriors.
They are filthy with froth, girdled in gore, combat-coarse
and crimson; they are drooping ball-bags; they are cows
with cocks.
And all the women of Ulster are like cows, does, mares
compared with me."

As soon as the women finished speaking, Loegaire and Conall
sprang into the hero light of their warrior frenzy, and they smashed
planks out of the side of the banquet hall to let their wives in. But
Cúchulainn lifted up the wall nearest him high enough that the
stars in the sky were visible beneath it, and his wife and her fifty
women and Fedelm and Lendabair and their two fifties were able
to enter. Then Cúchulainn dropped the wall so that it sank seven
feet into the ground. The whole building shook, toppling Bricriu's
sun parlour, and both Bricriu and his wife were pitched into the

dung of the dung pit in the middle of the courtyard among the dogs.

"Alas," said Bricriu. "Enemies have come to my fort."

He quickly picked himself up and saw that the banquet hall was lop-sided. He went in, but he was so filthy with the dog dung that the Ulstermen failed to recognise him until he spoke.

"It was my misfortune that I prepared a boar-feast for ye, Ulstermen," he said. "Dearer to me is my house than all my possessions. And so," he continued, "I put geis[7] on ye not to drink or eat or sleep until ye put my house back the way ye found it."

All the Ulster warriors tried to move the house but failed to raise it enough to let the wind pass between it and the ground. This presented a problem.

"I don't know what to suggest," said Sencha, "except that you should ask the one who made the house crooked to set it straight."

The Ulstermen asked Cúchulainn to straighten the house, and Bricriu said to him, "If you can't set it straight, king of the warriors of Ireland, no one in the world can."

So that the banqueters would not be without food and drink, Cúchulainn stood up and tried to raise the house but failed. Then his warp spasm came on him. A drop of blood appeared at the root of each strand of hair, and he pulled all his hair into his head so that from above it looked as if it had been shaved. He whirled like a wheel and stretched his body until there was enough space between each of his ribs to fit a warrior's foot. His might and power came on him then, and he heaved the house up until it was straight again.

The company relaxed and sat down to enjoy the feast: the kings and the chieftains on one side around far-famed Conor, the illustrious high king of Ulster, and their queens on the other side. But it wasn't long before the growing chatter of the women praising their husbands brought Conall and Loegaire and Cúchulainn to the brink of fighting once again. Sencha stood up and shook his olive branch, the Craobh Sencha, to get everyone's attention. He addressed the women – Emer standing at one end of the hall shoulder to shoulder with her fifty companions, and

---

[7] An injunction or prohibition that bound one by honour and/or magic.

Fedelm and Lendabair at the other end with their hundred – and intoned:

"I hereby place this restraint on ye,
splendid, excellent, noble ladies of Ulster:
cease your boastful words
so that your husbands' faces don't turn pale
in hard combat
through pride of prowess.
Women are to blame
for the shattering of shields,
the fighting of men,
the rivalry of great champions,
the raising of anger.
They are the cause of the habit of men
to do evil they cannot atone for
and demand what they cannot get.
I hereby place this restraint on ye,
splendid, excellent ladies."

Emer replied:
"I have a right to speak, Sencha, for I am the wife of a fine, experienced hero, who from the time of his training has combined form and intelligence without remiss. Among his warrior feats are the quick-breath feat, the apple feat, the phantom feat, the twisting trick, the feline feat, the unblemished blood-red raiment, the gai bolga,[8] the bold stroke, the birthing crush, the champion's shout, the wheel feat, the sword-edge feat, and climbing up spears and standing on their points.

"No man equals
his age and development and splendour
his speech and sagacity and breeding
his pleasantness and voice
his prowess, valour and weapon-skill

---

[8] A unique spring-loaded multi-barbed javelin thrust into the belly of an opponent.

his temper, triumph and turbulence
his graceful gait and accurate aim
his strength and swiftness
his slaughter of warrior-bands with the nine-fold feat.
There is no one like Cúchulainn."

"If what you say is true, woman," said Conall Cernach, "let's have that talented fellow come here and prove it."

"Absolutely not," said Cúchulainn. "I'm exhausted today, and until I finish eating and have a rest I'm not leaving the feast."

He was tired because it was on that day that he met the Grey of Macha on the slopes of Lindi Leith at Sliabh Fuait[9]. When the horse came out of the lake, Cúchulainn tamed him by grabbing him around the neck with both hands and struggling with him all around Ireland locked in combat, until he arrived that night at Emain Macha driving the horse in front of him. He also got the Black Sainglend in the same way from Loch Duib Sainglend.

Cúchulainn said, "Today the Grey and I travelled the great plains of Ireland: Bregia of Meath, marshy Muirthemne of Macha, the Plain of Maeve, the Curragh, Cletech Cerna, Lia Linn Locharna, the Plains of Fea, Femen and Fergna, Urros Domnand, Ros Roigne, and the Great Plain of Eo. It would be better for everyone that I eat and sleep before I do anything else. I swear by the god my people swear by, I will be fed and rested before I meet any man for sport and games."

"Very well," said Conor. "Let all the arguments cease until the feast is finished."

So there was peace for the remainder of the three days and three nights of the feast. But then the quarrel about the champion's portion started up again. Conor said, "Ye will go to Cú Roí mac Dáire and ask him to decide. He is an honest man who will give a true judgement, but there will be a price to pay for the service."

---

[9] A mountain near Newtown-Hamilton in County Armagh, also known as the Fews.

The Heroes Set Off for Cú Roí

Loegaire was the first. He went over the Plain of the Two Forks, the Gap of the Watcher, the Ford of Fergus' Chariot, the Ford of the Mórrígan, the Rowan Meadow of the Two Oxen in Clithar Fidbaidi in the Fews near the Meeting of the Four Roads beyond Dún Dealgan[10] across the Shelly Plain west to Sliabh Breg. At that point a heavy, dark, gloomy mist descended, confusing him so that he was not able to continue on his way.

Loegaire got down from the chariot and said to his charioteer, "We'll wait here until the mist clears up for us."

The charioteer turned the horses into a nearby meadow, where he saw a huge ogre coming toward him. He was not a pleasant sight: broad shoulders, wide mouth, bulging eyes, bristly beard, ugly, wrinkled, bushy-browed, horribly abominable. He was powerful, ruthless, dripping with arrogance, wanton, snorting, heavy-balled, strong of arm, bold. Every joint and member of his body from his shoulders to the ground was as black as coal. He was fierce, uncouth and misshapen.

He had dark grey, watery bloodshot eyes. His nose was broken in the middle and crooked with cavernous nostrils. The size of a fidchell[11] board was each green-yellow tooth set this way and that in his two jaws. A ship in full sail could slip through the mouth and the maw of that man. His hair was black and close-cropped except for a grisly lock that hung down beyond his shoulders like the tail of a wild horse.

His bowed, bent shin-bones could have been tree-stumps stripped and wrapped in salt-sacks. Long twisted sack-like thighs, knobby knees, feet as broad as shovels, arse the shape of a stew-pot – the man was uncommonly deformed. He wore a yellow-brown cloak, a short tunic that reached to his buttocks, and filthy old breeches down to his feet. The big killing blackthorn cudgel he carried on his back was the size of the shaft of a millwheel. A fat, furry lapdog was with him.

---

[10] Dundalk, County Louth.
[11] A board game like chess.

"Whose horses are these, lad?" he said, staring at the charioteer with contempt.

"The horses of Loegaire Buadach," he replied.

"Right," said the ogre. "It's a good man who looks after his horses."

As he spoke, he raised his cudgel and brought it down on the lad, beating him from ankle to head. He groaned and shouted. Loegaire came and said, "What have you done to the lad?"

"That's the penalty for the damage to the meadow," said the churl.

"I'll come to you myself," said Loegaire.

They began to fight, but Loegaire was soon forced to flee, and he ran until he reached Emain Macha, leaving behind his horses and chariot and charioteer and weapons.

Then Conall Cernach took the same road and arrived at the place where Loegaire had been forced to stop because of the magic mist. The fog was so dark, thick and heavy that Conall could not distinguish between earth and sky. He got down from his chariot, and his charioteer unharnessed the horses in the same meadow. It was not long before the lad saw the same ogre coming toward him. He asked the lad whose servant he was.

"I'm Conall Cernach's servant," he replied.

"A fine man," said the ogre, and he raised his hand and beat him from head to ankle. The lad cried out. Conall came and fought with the ogre until he was overcome just as Loegaire was, and he ran until he reached Emain Macha, leaving behind his weapons and chariot and charioteer and horses.

Cúchulainn took the same road until he reached the same place and encountered the same mist as the first two. He stepped down from his chariot, and Láeg took the horses into the meadow. It was not long before he saw the same man coming toward him, who asked whose servant he was.

"Cúchulainn's servant," he said.

"A fine man," said the ogre, belabouring him with the cudgel. Láeg cried out. Cúchulainn came, and he and the ogre closed and pummelled and pounded each other. Cúchulainn quickly defeated the ogre, and he took his horses and charioteer and those of the other two warriors to Emain Macha and gave them back to Loegaire and Conall.

"The champion's portion is yours," Bricriu said to Cúchulainn. To Loegaire and Conall he said, "It's clear from your deeds that you are not equal to him."

"That's not true, Bricriu," they said. "We know that he arranged with one of his friends from the Otherworld to play games with us regarding the champion's portion, and we won't relinquish it to him."

Conor and Fergus and the men of Ulster were unable to resolve the argument, and they decided to take the three heroes to Ailill and Maeve at Cruachan Aí to settle the question of the women's war of words and the champion's portion.

The Ulstermen Go to Cruachan Aí

They all set off except Cúchulainn, who stayed behind entertaining the women with nine apple feats, nine spear feats and nine knife feats, juggling all the pieces so that not one struck another. Láeg came to him and said, "You miserable wretch. Your power and prowess have passed away, and you've lost your chance for the champion's portion. The Ulstermen have already reached Cruachan."

"I hadn't noticed they'd left, Láeg," said Cúchulainn. "Prepare the chariot."

Láeg harnessed the horses and they set off. The Ulstermen had really only reached the Plain of Bregia by this time, and as Cúchulainn crossed Sliabh Fuait and the Plain of Bregia, the Grey of Macha and the Black Sainglend galloped so fast that the last chariot to leave the banquet hall was the first to arrive at Cruachan Aí.

The urgency of the Ulstermen and the violent velocity of their going so shook the royal house that the weapons tumbled from the walls and clattered to the floor, the watchers in the keep swayed like rushes in a stream, and Maeve said, "There is thunder but no clouds." Findabair, daughter of Ailill and Maeve, went to the sun porch over the gate of the fortress.

"I see a chariot coming over the plain," she said.

"Describe the form of the man, the colour of the horses and the chariot's way of going," said Maeve.

"I see two horses pulling the chariot," said the girl. "Two matching fiery dapple greys with ears pricked, thin-muzzled, broad-chested, slim-flanked. A wicker chariot with inlays and black wheels and a hardwood tongue as straight as a sword. A man with fair curly hair is in the chariot. His hair is braided with three colours: brown at the back of his head, blood-red in the middle, and a circlet of yellow-gold hair wrapped around the end. Three concentric bands around his head. A fine crimson cloak with five silver discs on it wrapped about him. A shield fit for battle with a burnished bronze edge and a five-pointed boss spike flames in his fist. A canopy of wild birds over his chariot."

"I know that man by his description," said Maeve.

> "A champion of kings,
> deserving of victory,
> deadly warrior,
> fire of doom,
> avenging crusher,
> dragon-hearted,
> Brown Mouse,
> red-hand Loegaire of the swift, sharp sword-edge shaves
> and ground-swells of return strokes.

"I swear by the oath my people swear by, if Loegaire Buadach comes at us with hostile anger we'll be like leeks cut to the ground with a keen blade unless we do what he wants."

"I see another chariot coming over the plain," said Findabair.

"Describe the form of the man, the colour of the horses and the chariot's way of going," said Maeve.

"I see two horses pulling the chariot," said the girl. "One is a white-faced hardy roan, swift as an arrow, leaping like a wild deer, wearing a breastplate that strikes vigorous strokes of victory. He bounds across fords, estuaries, passes, scrub land and plains like a flock of birds faster than my eye can follow. The other horse is a feisty, vicious chestnut with a thick, wavy mane, broad chest,

45

broad back, slender flank, powerful quarters. He is master of the territory between plains – the wilderness and the wasteland – but just as easily takes a warrior over roads. The chariot is made of spruce with fine bronze inlaid circles, the shaft covered with silver, the yoke grandly filigreed, both bridles richly gold-chased. A man with fair curly hair is in the chariot. His face is half-red and half-white. He wears an open white tunic and a blue and deep purple cloak and carries a brown shield bronze-edged with a yellow boss. A red fiery spear flames in his fist. A canopy of wild birds over his chariot."

"I know the man by his description," said Maeve.

"A roaring lion
a fierce lynx
pillar of pillages
triumph over the trembling
harsh heaper
of head upon head
feat upon feat
combat upon combat.
Dispute turns to destruction:
the likes of the slaughter of a trout on red sand –
such would be the raging wrath
the son of Findchóem wreaks upon us.

"I swear by the oath my people swear by, like a trout slaughtered on a red-hot stone with iron flails will Conall Cernach slice us into small slivers in his superhuman fury."

"I see another chariot coming across the plain."

"Describe the form of the man, the colour of the horses and the chariot's way of going," said Maeve.

"I see two horses pulling the chariot," said the girl. "A grey horse broad of haunch and hip, swift-moving, lynx-lithe, long flowing tail, mighty stormy arched mane, high-headed, broad-chested. From beneath his forceful feet flaming sods flare forth. His four fleet hooves speed fiercely past fast-flying feathered flocks to win the race and take the prize. Steam streams from the spectral steed; his bitted mouth spouts blazing sparks.

46

"The other horse is a spirited jet-black, hard-headed, sturdy, noble strong-haunched stayer with a quick turn of foot, a thick wavy mane and full-flowing tail. After a battle, he goes racing around the land, galloping through glens and over grasslands. He draws an inlaid wicker chariot with bronze frame-work, gold-plated yoke and yellow iron gold-plated wheels, bright gold fringe on the bridles.

"The dark, blood-stained man in the chariot is foremost of the men of Ireland. He wears a fine-fashioned crimson tunic. An inlaid gold brooch clasps his cloak and beats against his fair breast in warrior rhythm. Eight red dragon-stone pupils in the centres of his two eyes. Two glowing blood-red blue-veined cheeks spout sparks and steam. He performs the high hero leap into the air and nine warrior feats above the chariot."

"This is surely a drop before a shower," said Maeve. "I know that man by his description.

"He is a millstone of the ocean,
a surging sea monster,
a gory grinder,
a great bear of a tidal wave,
a mighty blazing beast,
a brutal bringer of battle, odds-on onslaughts, colossal carnage.
He is a fighting fiend,
a dealer of death and destruction who heaps deed upon deed and head upon head.
That is precisely how the poets describe Cúchulainn. His mill will mince us to morsels.

"I swear by the oath my people swear by, if Cúchulainn comes at us in fierce fury like a ten-blade millwheel mashing malt, that man alone could grind us to sand and soil unless we cool his fire and calm his frenzy."

A sound like thunder splitting the air and stormy seas shaking the earth announced the approach of the rest of the Ulstermen's chariots to Cruachan Aí. Maeve called to her people:

47

"Bring out good-looking naked women to greet them: bare-breasted, completely nude and sexy: maidens willing to be friendly and mate with the visitors – citadels with their passages lying open. Prepare vats of cold water and couches, plenty of fresh food, the best of our own stock of intoxicating malt liquor. If they've come to do battle, they won't be so likely to kill us."

Maeve went out the gate into the courtyard with 150 maidens and placed three vats of cold water in front of the three heroes to cool them down. She then asked if they would prefer one house each or one for the three of them.

"A separate house for each of us," said Cúchulainn.

They selected the women they preferred and took them into the houses, which were furnished with sumptuous beds. Cúchulainn chose Findabair, daughter of Maeve and Ailill. Then Maeve and Ailill went out with their entire household to greet Conor and the rest of the Ulstermen as they arrived.

"This is pleasing to us," said Sencha in response to their welcome.

The Ulstermen were brought into the fort and given free run of the palace, with its seven courts and seven compartments between the fire and the wall. There were bronze facings and red yew carvings, three bronze slats in the roof vault. The house was made of oak with a slate roof and glass windows. Maeve and Ailill's compartment, with silver facings and bronze strips and a silver staff, was in the centre of the house so Ailill could see everyone. Great feasts were prepared, and the Ulstermen stayed for three days and three nights.

Then Ailill asked the Ulstermen why they had come, and Sencha explained about the heroes' contention for the champion's portion and the ladies' rivalry over precedence. "And they refused to accept any judgement but yours," he added.

Ailill was amazed, and he was not happy in his mind. "I see no reason for this dispute to be brought before me," he said, "unless it is out of mischief."

"Surely there is no better person than yourself to make this decision," said Sencha.

"I'd like to ponder this a while," said Ailill.

"We need our champions," said Sencha, "for they are worth more than lesser men."

"Three days and three nights will be enough, then," said Ailill.

"That won't strain our friendship," said Sencha, and the Ulstermen departed, bestowing their blessings on Ailill and Maeve and their curse on Bricriu, for it was he who caused the dispute. Loegaire, Conall and Cúchulainn remained behind to await Ailill's judgement.

That night, while they were eating, three demon cats were set loose from the Cave of Cruachan and attacked them. Loegaire and Conall climbed into the rafters, leaving their food with the beasts, and stayed there till morning. Cúchulainn didn't move from his place when the cat approached him. When it stretched out its neck toward the food, he struck it on the head with his sword, which glanced off as if it were a stone. The cat sat down, and Cúchulainn neither ate nor slept until morning. Then the cats left.

When Ailill came in and saw Loegaire and Conall still in the rafters and Cúchulainn sitting at the table, he said, "Is this not enough of a judgement in itself?"

"It's not against animals that we fight, but humans," said Loegaire and Conall.

Ailill went into his apartment and sat with his back against the wall, uneasy in his mind and perplexed about what to do. He didn't sleep or eat for three days and three nights. Finally, Maeve said, "You're being too timid. If you don't decide, I will."

"It's difficult for me, this judgement," he said. "It's a bitter task they've given me."

"It's not difficult at all," said Maeve. "Comparing Loegaire to Conall is like comparing bronze to silver, and comparing Conall to Cúchulainn is like comparing silver to gold."

She summoned Loegaire and said, "Welcome, Loegaire the Victorious. It is proper to award you the champion's portion, the title of King of the Warriors of Ireland forever, and this bronze goblet with a silver bird at the bottom as proof of our decision. But let no one see it until you are at the Red Branch Hall at Emain Macha and they bring out the champion's portion. Then, when all the nobles of Ulster are assembled, take out the goblet and show it

49

to them, so that they will know it is proof that the champion's portion belongs to you, and no one will dispute it."

Then she filled the goblet with wine and gave it to him. Loegaire drank it all down in one gulp, and Maeve said, "That is truly the feast of a champion. May your name and fame be celebrated by the warriors of Ulster for a hundred hundred years."

Loegaire took his leave, and Maeve summoned Conall Cernach and recited the same speech she had made to Loegaire.

"Welcome, Conall the Triumphant. It is proper to award you the champion's portion, the title of King of the Warriors of Ireland forever, and this silver goblet with a gold bird at the bottom as proof of our decision. But let no one see it until you are at the Red Branch Hall at Emain Macha and they bring out the champion's portion. Then, when all the nobles of Ulster are assembled, take out the goblet and show it to them, so that they will know it is proof that the champion's portion belongs to you, and no one will dispute it."

Then she filled the goblet with wine and gave it to him. Conall drank it all down in one gulp, Maeve said, "May your name and fame be celebrated by the warriors of Ulster for a hundred hundred years." Conall took his leave, and she sent for Cúchulainn.

Cúchulainn was playing fidchell with Láeg mac Ríangabra, his charioteer, when the messenger arrived and said, "Come and speak with the king and the queen."

"You're making fun of me," he said. "Take your lies to some other fool."

He threw one of the fidchell pieces at the messenger, hitting him in the centre of the forehead. He fell dead between Ailill and Maeve.

"Alas," said Maeve, "how Cúchulainn's warrior fury brings on the slaughter."

She went to him and wrapped her arms around his neck.

"Take your lies to someone else," he said.

"Wondrous son of Ulster," said Maeve, "dazzling hero of Ireland, there are no lies between us. If all the warriors of Ireland came, it is to you we would give the prize, for the men of Ireland acknowledge your superiority in fame and fighting skills, brilliance and nobility."

Cúchulainn stood up and followed Maeve into the palace, where Ailill greeted him with a hearty welcome. He gave him a gold goblet filled with their best wine with a bird made of precious stone at the bottom, and a dragon-stone as big as his two eyes.

"Here, now," said Maeve, "is truly the champion's portion for you. May your name and fame be celebrated by the warriors of Ulster for a hundred hundred years."

"As well as that," said Ailill and Maeve, "it is our judgement that just as you have no equal among the warriors of Ulster, neither do any of the Ulsterwomen compare to your wife, and so she should precede them into the banquet hall."

Cúchulainn drank to that, draining the goblet, and said farewell to the king and queen and their household and left with his chariot driver, Láeg.

[The *Lebor na hUidre* compiler has inserted a series of incidents that delay the return of the three heroes to Emain Macha. To relate them in full would slow the narrative too much, so they are summarised here.]

But then Maeve changed her mind and decided to test the three heroes further. She called them back, and they unharnessed their horses. They returned to their separate accommodations, where Loegaire was entertained by Conchend, daughter of Cet mac Mágach, and her fifty maidens, Conall was accompanied by Sive the Eloquent, daughter of Maeve and Ailill, and her fifty, and Cúchulainn enjoyed the presence of Maeve and Ailill's daughter Findabair with her fifty. Maeve herself visited Cúchulainn as well.

In the morning, Cúchulainn assembled the 150 female attendants to show them a trick. He collected a needle from each of them and threw the needles into the air at the same time in such a way that each needle went into the eye of another so that they were all joined together. Then he caught the needles and returned each one to its proper owner.

Maeve told them to go to her foster father and step-mother, Ercol and Garmna, who sent them to Samera who sent them to the Amazons of the Glen. Loegaire went to the Amazons first. They defeated him, stripped his clothes off and took away his weapons.

51

Conall was next. He kept his clothes and his sword but lost his other weapons. Cúchulainn was on the point of defeat when Láeg abused him for his weakness. Cúchulainn's battle frenzy came on him, and he hacked and smashed the Amazons until the Glen ran with blood. Samera confirmed that Cúchulainn deserved the champion's portion and that Emer should have precedence over the Ulsterwomen.

The three warriors returned to Ercol, who fought and defeated Loegaire and Conall and was beaten and taken captive by Cúchulainn and carried to Emain Macha. When Loegaire, Conall and Cúchulainn arrived, no one dared ask about the outcome of their visit to Ailill and Maeve.

The Ulstermen were assembled in the Mead Hall, and it was Cúchulainn's father, Sualtam mac Róich, who was in charge of serving. The champion's portion was withheld when the servers began to distribute the rest of the food, and Dubtach Chafer-tongue said, "Why is the champion's portion not presented to one of these noble warriors, since those three returned from Cruachan with no report of a decision by Ailill as to which of them should get it?"

Loegaire stood and raised the bronze goblet with the silver bird at the bottom and said, "The champion's portion is mine, and no one will take it from me."

"It's not yours," said Conall Cernach. "They gave you a bronze goblet and they gave me a silver one. The difference between them clearly shows that the champion's portion belongs to me."

"It doesn't belong to either of ye," said Cúchulainn, standing up. "Ye have brought no proof that the champion's portion has been awarded to either of ye. The king and queen had no wish to incur your hostility by adding fire to the flames. Ye both deserve the prizes ye got, but the champion's portion is mine, because I'm the one who got the best prize."

He held up the gold goblet with the bird made of precious stone at the bottom, and the dragon-stone as big as his two eyes, so that Conor and all the nobles of Ulster could see it.

"The champion's portion is mine by right," he added, "unless someone can take it from me by force."

"We all agree," said Conor and Fergus and all the Ulster nobles together. "The champion's portion is yours by the decision of Ailill and Maeve."

"I swear by the oath my people swear by," said Loegaire and Conall, "that is not an unbought goblet you got. You bribed Ailill and Maeve with jewels and other gifts so they would give the champion's portion to you and no one else."

"I swear by the oath my people swear by," said Conall, "I don't respect that judgement, and you will not have the champion's portion."

All three leapt up and drew their swords. Conor and Fergus came between them and grabbed their hands and made them put their swords down.

"Stop," said Sencha, "and do what I tell you."

"We will," they said.

[The *Lebor na hUidre* compiler here inserts an episode that duplicates, dilutes and spoils the ending. The three heroes are sent to Yellow, who sends them on to Terror, who tests them and confirms Cúchulainn's right to the champion's portion. On their return to Emain Macha, Loegaire and Conall refuse to accept that judgement, and they are sent once again to Cú Roí mac Dáire.]

The Heroes Set Off Again for Cú Roí

Cú Roí was not at home when they arrived – he was away in the lands of Scythia – but he knew they were coming, so he had left word with his wife, Bláthnat, daughter of Mind, to make them welcome. She did so, and then she told them that Cú Roí wanted them to take turns, according to seniority, guarding the castle at night until he returned. In whatever part of the world Cú Roí happened to be, each night he would cast a spell on his castle to make it revolve as fast as a millstone so no one could find the door to attack after sunset. As Loegaire Buadach was the eldest, he stood guard the first night.

He sat watching until dawn, when he saw an ogre approaching from a distance across the western sea. He was huge and ugly and terrifying. He seemed as tall as the sky, and Loegaire could see the shimmer of the sea between his legs. In each hand he carried a wagon-load of stripped oak trees. He threw one of them at Loegaire, who dodged it, and then three more, none of which hit Loegaire or his shield. Then Loegaire threw a spear and missed.

The ogre reached out a hand as broad as a field toward Loegaire and grabbed him. As big and strong as Loegaire was, he fitted into the ogre's hand as if he were a year-old child. The ogre twirled him between the palms of his hands like a fidchell-piece swept along a millrace, and threw him over the wall of the fort. He landed half-dead in the dung heap outside. There was no opening in the fort at that point, and all the men inside thought he had leapt over the wall as a challenge to them to match his feat. They tried to do it till the end of the day without success.

Conall Cernach, being older than Cúchulainn, took the next night's watch, and the same thing happened to him that happened to Loegaire.

On the third night, Cúchulainn sat in the watch seat. The three Greys of the Cold-flesh Swamp, the three Mad Oxen of Bregia, and the three sons of Mighty Fist of Music arrived to make a slaughter in the fort. This was also the night it was prophesied that the monster that lived in the lake next to the fort would eat all the people and animals inside. Cúchulainn felt a foreboding of evil as he sat watching. About midnight he heard the loud racket of something approaching.

"Hallo, hallo," he called out. "Who's there? If ye are friends, stay where ye are. If ye are enemies, go away."

They screeched at him, and he jumped on them and left all nine dead on the ground. Then he piled their heads any which way into the watch seat and resumed his vigil. Nine more screeched at him, and another nine. He treated them the same way and heaped all the heads and the spoils in one cairn. He stayed there till the end of the night, tired, weak and weary. Then from the lake came the sound of a crashing sea, and he went to see what had caused it. He saw a water monster about fifteen metres long rising from the lake. It rose into the air and leapt toward the castle, opening its mouth to engulf one of the royal houses.

Cúchulainn used his swooping feat, leaping high in the air, and went as quick as a whirling wheel around the monster. He wrapped his arms around the beast's throat, reached his hand into its gullet, tore out its heart, and threw the body to the ground. Then he took his sword and chopped it to pieces and threw the head into the watch seat with the others.

He rested broken and miserable until dawn, when he saw coming toward him from over the sea the same ogre that had attacked Loegaire and Conall.

"Bad night tonight," said the ogre.

"And a worse one to yourself, you churl," replied Cúchulainn.

The ogre threw one of the stripped oak trees at him, but he dodged it and three more. Cúchulainn threw his javelin at him and missed. The ogre reached out a hand to grab him as he had the others, but Cúchulainn did his salmon leap and his swooping feat with his sword over the ogre's head as quick as a wild animal. Round and round he went like a water-wheel, till the ogre was dizzy.

"A life for a life, Cúchulainn," said the ogre.

"Give me my three demands," said Cúchulainn.

"They're yours, if you can say them in one breath."

"The title of King of the Warriors of Ireland for me forever, the champion's portion for me without contention, and my wife always to take precedence over all the women of Ulster."

"It shall be so from now on," said the ogre, and he disappeared.

Cúchulainn fell to pondering over the leaps he thought Loegaire and Conall had made over the wall, not knowing that the ogre had thrown them over. He tried to do the leap twice and failed, which made him think he was now unworthy of the champion's portion because Loegaire and Conall were able to do something he could not. He stepped back and jumped against the wall, striking his forehead on it. Then he jumped so high he could see the whole fort below him. And finally he fell into such a rage that he stepped right over the wall and landed by the front door. His two footprints can still be seen in the flagstone. He then went into the house and heaved a sigh.

Bláthnat was well aware of the trials Cúchulainn had undergone that night. She said, "That's truly not a sigh of shame; it's a sigh of triumph and victory."

They saw Cú Roí coming into the house with the battle spoils of the three nines Cúchulainn had killed, along with their heads and the head of the monster. He threw them in a heap on the floor and said, "The lad who collected all these trophies in one night is a lad worthy to guard a king's fort permanently. [12]

"Of ye who have contended, the champion's portion belongs by right to Cúchulainn above all other warriors of Ireland. Not even the bravest of them could match him in collecting this many trophies."

And so it was the judgement of Cú Roí that the champion's portion belonged to Cúchulainn over all the warriors of the Gael, and that his wife was first over all the Ulsterwomen in the banquet hall. He also gave him the value of 21 cows in gold and silver as a reward for his night's work.

Then Loegaire, Conall and Cúchulainn took their leave of Cú Roí and arrived at Emain Macha before the end of the day. At the dinner that night, the servers held back the champion's portion when they distributed the food.

"We see," said Dubtach Chafer-tongue, "that there is no contention among ye tonight for the champion's portion. Perhaps the one ye went to consult has given his decision?"

The other warriors spoke up and said to Cúchulainn, "The champion's portion wasn't awarded to any of ye. And if it was, Cúchulainn hasn't revealed it since they arrived at Emain Macha."

Cúchulainn said that he wasn't at all eager to compete for the champion's portion, because it wasn't worth it if the resulting loss outweighed the benefit. For that reason the distributing of the champion's portion was not decided until –

---

[12] A champion is not only the winner of a competition but also the personal bodyguard of a king: the warrior who protects the king in battle and takes his place in a challenge.

The Compact of the Champions at Emain Macha

One time the Ulstermen were in Emain Macha relaxing after a day of games. Conor and Fergus mac Róich and the nobles of Ulster came into the Red Branch Hall from the sports field. Cúchulainn and Loegaire Buadach and Conall Cernach weren't there that night, but the cream of the rest of the Ulster warriors were.

At dusk, they saw a huge, hideous giant enter the hall. He was at least twice the size of any of the Ulster warriors, ugly and terrifying. He was dressed in an old stinking untanned animal skin and a dull grey cloak, and his head of hair was so big and thick there was room for thirty calves to shelter under it. Bulging from his head were two fierce yellow eyes, each the size of a cauldron big enough to cook an ox. Thick as the upper arm of an ordinary man was each of his fingers. In his left hand he carried a chopping-block that was the load of a twenty-ox team. In his right hand an axe the weight of three ingots of iron. It would take a six-ox plough team to move it. The razor-sharp edge would cut hairs blown against it. He walked over to the fireplace and stood under the chimney arch in front of the fire.

"Is the hall so small for you," said Dubtach Chafer-tongue, "that you have to stand under the arch in front of the fire, or do you intend to outshine the chandelier? In that case, the hall will go on fire before the household is illuminated."

The giant replied, "Whatever my abilities, you will find that my height will be kept under control so that the household is enlightened without the hall burning down. But that's not my only talent; I have others besides.

"I have travelled all over Ireland, Scotland, Europe, Africa, Asia, Greece, Sythia, the Orkney Islands, and to the Pillars of Hercules, the Tower of Breogán and the Island of Cádiz," he said, "and I have not found anywhere a man who will give me fair play. But since ye Ulstermen surpass the warriors of all those other countries in strength, valour and prowess, in nobility, pride and dignity, and in justice, generosity and overall excellence, I thought

I might find one man among ye who would undertake this matter with me."

"It's not right," said Fergus mac Róich, "that the good name of a province be put at risk because of one man failing to prove his honour. Perhaps death is no nearer to him than it is to you."

"I don't try to evade it," he said.

"Then tell us what your quest is," said Fergus.

"Only if fair play is guaranteed to me," he replied.

"It is proper to guarantee fair play," said Sencha, "for it is not acceptable for a great people to break sureties pledged to a single man. It seems to us that if you find such a man as you are seeking, you will find the one who fits the description here among us."

"I exempt Conor because he is king," said the stranger, "and likewise Fergus because of his rank. Apart from those two, I invite any of ye warriors to agree to my proposition: that I cut off his head tonight, and he can cut off mine tomorrow night."

"In that case, there is no warrior here apart from those two," said Dubtach.

"There is now," shouted Muinremur, as he leapt forward. He had the strength of a hundred battle-hardened soldiers, with the might of a hundred hero-blows in each forearm. "Bend down, you clown," he said, "so that I can cut off *your* head tonight, and then tomorrow night you can cut off *mine*."

"If that was the proposition I wanted," said the giant, "I could have got it anywhere. We'll do it according to my challenge: I cut off your head tonight, and you cut off mine tomorrow night."

"I swear by my people," Dubtach said to the giant, "there's no risk of death for you – the man dead tonight attacking you tomorrow. Only you, if you have the magic power, can be killed every night and take revenge the following day."

"Very well, then," said the giant to Muinremur. "We'll do it your way. But I hold you to your promise to return tomorrow and fulfil your part of the agreement."

Muinremur took the axe from the giant. It measured seven feet along the edge. The giant placed his neck on the chopping block. Muinremur brought the axe down so that it went through the neck into the block. The head landed at the base of the chimney arch, and the house was filled with blood. The giant stood up, picked up his head, axe and chopping block, and, holding them to his chest, walked out of the hall, blood pouring out of his neck and flowing through the hall. The people were stunned and horrified.

"I swear by my people," said Dubtach, "if that giant comes back tomorrow night after being killed tonight, he won't leave a man alive."

The giant returned the following night, but Muinremur was absent.

"It's not fair that Muinremur failed to keep his word," the giant said. "Which of those who contend for the champion's portion of Ulster is here tonight? Where is Loegaire Buadach?"

"I'm here," said Loegaire.

Loegaire made the same pledge as Muinremur and likewise failed to return the following night. His excuse was, "What is there to be said, when a man with a right to get it has come to ask for your head?" according to Yeats's verse play *The Green Helmet*. The same thing occurred with Conall Cernach the next night.

On the fourth night, all the women of Ulster were in the Red Branch Hall to see the strange happenings they had heard about. And Cúchulainn was there. When the giant arrived, he was furious.

"Ulstermen," he said, "your courage and competence are gone. Your warriors want the champion's portion but won't contest it. Where is that miserable backward squinter Cúchulainn? I'd like to know if his word is worth more than that of the other heroes."

"I don't wish to accept your challenge," said Cúchulainn.

"You wretched flea," said the giant. "I think you're just terrified of death."

Cúchulainn got up and went to him, picked up the axe, and chopped off his head with such force that it sailed up into the rafters, shaking the house. Then he grabbed the head and smashed it with the axe. The giant stood up, collected his head, axe and chopping block, and left.

The following night, the Ulstermen wondered if Cúchulainn would back out of the agreement, as they saw that he was depressed, and they thought it might be appropriate to sing his death-song. They were sure his life would last only until the giant arrived.

Then Cúchulainn said to Conor to lessen his shame: "Take my sword and shield, and don't leave until I have fulfilled my compact with the giant. Death is hanging over my head, and I would rather have death with honour."

At the end of the day they saw the giant approaching.

"Where is Cúchulainn?" he said.

"I am here, to be sure."

"Your speech sounds depressed tonight, you wretch," the giant said. "You are afraid of death. But however great is your fear of death, you have not failed to keep our appointment."

Cúchulainn went to him and stretched his neck across the chopping block, but the block was so wide that his neck only reached half-way.

"Stretch out your neck, you miserable runt," said the giant.

"You're tormenting me," said Cúchulainn. "Give me my death quickly. I didn't torment you last night. I swear if you keep tormenting me I'll have grounds for complaint."

"I can't cut off your head because of the width of the block and the shortness of your neck and body." (Cúchulainn is always described as being shorter than the average man.)

Cúchulainn stretched his neck and his whole body so that a warrior's foot would fit between his ribs, and his head reached the other side of the block. The giant raised the axe till it reached the rafters. The creaking of the old animal skin he wore and the swish of the axe as it sliced through the air sounded like the wind in the trees on a stormy night. Down came the axe-head until it stopped, with the edge reversed, just before it struck Cúchulainn's neck.

"Arise, Cúchulainn," said the giant. "Of all the warriors of Ulster and Ireland, whatever their courage, none compare with you for valour, prowess and honour. I hereby bestow on you henceforth the title of King of the Warriors of Ireland, the right to the champion's portion without opposition, and the precedence of your wife over the women of Ulster on entering the mead hall forever. Whoever contends against you now, I swear by the oath my people swear by, he will have a short life."

And then the giant disappeared. It was Cú Roí mac Dáire, who had come to enforce the judgement he had given to Cúchulainn.

The Bórama
(The Cattle Tribute)

The imposing of the Cattle Tribute on the Leinstermen by the Uí Néill kings of Tara is the thread uniting a series of historical and legendary incidents spanning more than 900 years. Main sources: *The Book of Leinster* and *The Book of Lecan*. The appended 10th-century "Battle of Allen", which includes "The Head of Donn Bó", from the 14th-century *Yellow Book of Lecan*, is not part of the 11th-century Bórama proper.

Tuathal Techmar

In the middle of the first century AD, the vassal tribes revolted and killed the high king, Feradach Finnfechtnach ("the Brightly Prosperous") and his son Fiacha Fionnfholaidh ("of the White Kine"), and then ruled for thirty years. The grandson of Feradach was Tuathal Techmar, whose mother was the daughter of the King of Scotland.

Tuathal was born in Scotland, his mother being pregnant and having taken refuge there with her family after her husband was killed, and he spent the first 25 years of his life there. From Scotland or Britain he brought help – possibly Romans (see Notes) – to Ireland in order to defeat the rebels and restore the kingship to the royal line in the person of himself. In the process, he fought 25 battles each against Leinster, Ulster and Connacht, and 35 against Munster.

When the fighting was over, Tuathal held the Feast of Tara, where he made the provincial kings pledge by the solemn vow of the elements that they and their descendants would never "to all eternity strive for Ireland's sovereignty" against him or his descendants. One of his descendants was Niall Naoighiallach ("of the Nine Hostages"), for whom the Uí Néill are named.

Eochaid Doimlén of Ráth Imáil near the Glen of Imaal, King of Leinster, was at that Feast, and he was without a wife. Tuathal Techmar had two marriageable daughters: Fithir, foster daughter of Conrach king of Connacht, and Dáirine, foster daughter of Fergus king of Ulster. While blood relations frequently were killed for the kingship, it was not acceptable to kill someone to whom one was related by marriage, so it was obviously to the advantage of both Tuathal and Eochaid for Eochaid to marry one of Tuathal's daughters. Eochaid preferred Dáirine, the younger of the two, and asked for her hand.

"I will be happy to have you as my son-in-law," said Tuathal, "but it is not right for the younger daughter to be married before her sister. You may have Fithir."

So Eochaid married Fithir and took her back to Ráth Imáil. When his people saw her, they told him he should have chosen Dáirine, "the fayrer Daughter & better nurtured & brought up",[13] and he agreed. He sent a message to Tuathal Techmar:

"I regret to inform you that my wife, your daughter Fithir, has died. Now please can I marry Dáirine?"

Tuathal replied: "If I had fifty-one daughters, they would all be given to you until one of them was found suitable." And he sent Dáirine to Eochaid. As soon as Fithir saw that she was to be replaced by her sister, she died of shame. When Dáirine saw that Fithir was dead, she died of grief.

The Imposing of the Tribute

It was not long before Tuathal learned the truth of what had happened. He sent word to Conrach of Connacht and Fergus of Ulster that their foster daughters were dead because of Eochaid. Conrach and Fergus gathered their warriors and came to Tara. Tuathal asked them what they thought should be done, and they both answered that nothing would satisfy them but battle with Leinster.

---

[13] *Annals of Clonmacnoise*, p. 53.

Their combined forces numbered 12,000 – some say 22,000. Leinster fielded 9,000. The invaders attacked and burned some of Leinster's major settlements and places of assembly: Naas, Dún Aillen, Mullaghmast, Mullaghreelion and Báirc Bresail. The final battle was at Ráth Imáil, where Eochaid was shortened by a head. Tuathal installed Eochaid's half-brother Erc as king of Leinster and imposed the Cattle Tribute as an *eric* or compensation for the deaths of his daughters, to be paid annually: 5000 (some say 15,000) each of cows, pigs, sheep, mantles, silver chains, and copper cauldrons; one copper cauldron large enough to hold twelve pigs and twelve cows; thirty red-eared cows and their calves with gold-bossed halters and spancels.

This first taking of the Tribute has been dated to AD 90. It was demanded of Leinster by more than forty high kings over the next 600 years of the saga proper and for another 300 years beyond that, though not always successfully. Tuathal ruled for thirty years from AD 76 until he was killed at the age of "110" (probably about 60) by Mael mac Rochraide, King of Ulster, who succeeded Tuathal. Mael took the Tribute. Tuathal's son Felim Rechtaidh ("the Legist") took it when Cú Corb, founder of Maelodrán's tribe, was king of Leinster, and he killed Cú Corb.[14] Felim's son, Conn Céadchathach ("of the Hundred Battles"), took it once, but in the 2nd-century Battle of Maistiu (the Rath of Mullaghmast in County Kildare) Conn was defeated by Eochaid mac Earca, who then held the high kingship for seven years until Conn recovered it. Conn's son-in-law Conaire took the Tribute, and Art mac Conn had to fight to get it.

The *Claenfherta* (Sloping Trenches) of Tara

During the reign of Art's son, Cormac mac Airt, Dunlaing son of Enna Nia killed thirty princesses and their 3000 handmaidens at

---

[14] Felim also "eloped" with Cú Corb's wife, Maeve of the Red Side, a sovereignty-goddess figure of Leinster and Tara who "would not permit any king in Temair (Tara) without his having herself as wife" (MS Mat., p. 480).

the Hill of Tara in 241. This outrage caused the slipping of the mounds – the Sloping Trenches – on the northwest corner of Tara. Cormac executed twelve Leinster chiefs and levied the Tribute as compensation.

The Battle of Cnámros ("Bonewood")[15]

Cairbre Lifechair, son of Cormac mac Airt, demanded the Tribute of his cousin Bresal Bélach. Bresal refused to pay it, and he gathered the Leinstermen at Ráth Imáil and asked for their advice. They recommended that Bresal call on fellow Leinsterman Fionn mac Cumhaill and the Fianna to lend a helping hand. Bresal did so, and Fionn mustered 46,500 warriors: 1500 officers commanding 30 men each. Greatly outnumbered, Cairbre was not able to take the Tribute. Nine thousand of his men were killed, including his three sons. This is probably one of the motives for Cairbre's subsequent attack on the Fianna in the Battle of Gabhra (Garristown, County Meath) in 284, which resulted in the destruction of the Fianna.

During the next two centuries, several high kings tried to impose the Tribute, and among those unsuccessful was the great Niall of the Nine Hostages, who tried and failed twelve times. Dunlaing's son resisted the imposition of the Tribute twenty-eight times with the aid of Saint Brigit, who also helped the Leinstermen in the Battle of Finnabair in 535 and the Battle of Allen in 722 (see below).

The Battle of Áth Dara (458)

Laeghaire, son of Niall of the Nine Hostages and high king 428-462, promised his father that he would never abandon the old gods of Ireland for the Christian God. One of the best-known legends of Saint Patrick tells of Laeghaire's apparent conversion to

---

[15] Probably Camross, Co. Laois.

64

Christianity after Patrick challenged the power of the druids by lighting the "Paschal fire" on the Hill of Slane. Laeghaire's misadventure in the saga of the Bórama suggests that he remained an unreconstructed pagan, unless as a committed Christian he felt he could safely violate a pagan vow.

Bresal Bélach's grandson Enna Cinnselach ("the Quarrelsome") was king of Leinster when Laeghaire imposed the Tribute for no evident reason except that it had been done by high kings before him, and he himself had done it successfully more than once. At the Battle of Áth Dara, or Adare, on the River Barrow, Laeghaire was defeated, "and a 'red slaughter' of Conn's Half [Laeghaire's Uí Néill forces] made, and their heads collected so that in *magh Ailbhe* or 'Moyalvy' on the Barrow-side a cairn of them was made".[16]

Laeghaire was captured, and he was allowed to return home with his head still on his shoulders on condition that he swear a powerful pagan vow by the elements – by sun and moon, water and air, day and night, sea and land – that he would never again attempt to impose the Tribute. Two years later he took cattle in Leinster territory near Carbury Hill in County Kildare. Although this foray seems to have been a *crech* or minor cattle raid rather than an imposition of the Tribute, it was deemed a violation of his vow, and he was cursed to die "between Éire and Alba", the Irish names for Ireland and Scotland: *"Talam dá shlucud ocus grian dá loscud ocus gaeth do dula uad* – Earth to swallow him, Sun to scorch him, Wind (his breath) to pass away from him."[17]

Laeghaire thought he could avoid the curse by never going to sea between Ireland and Scotland. In 462, he was marching through the Bog of Allen in Kildare between two hillocks 65 feet and 40 feet above the surface of the bog. The hillocks, north-northeast of Rathangan, are now called Lullymore and Lullybeg, but at that time they were known locally as Éire and Alba. He was struck by lightning *"etir in da chnoc .i. Eiriu ocus Albu a n-anmanda i taeb Chaise* – between the two hills called Eire and

---

[16] O'Grady, *Silva Gadelica*, p. 407.
[17] Ibid.

Alba by the side of the Cas". The Cushaling, formerly Cashalin, River is nearby.[18]

The elements of God, which he had pledged as guarantee,
Inflicted the doom of death on the king.
Chronicum Scotorum

Laeghaire is buried on the Hill of Tara at Ráth Laeghaire, in a standing position facing south against Leinster. The next forty battles over the Tribute were mainly won by the Leinstermen.

The Battle of Finnabair (535)

The annals report that the Battle of Finnabair was won against the Uí Néill by the corpse of the Leinster king Illann, who lived for 120 years. Illann died before the Uí Néill attacked – reliable sources say he died in 527 – but he had been granted "the gift of victory" by Saint Brigit. Reasoning that Brigit's gift still remained in Illann's body, the Leinstermen carried it into battle with them.[19]

The Death of Cummascach (595)

Aed Ainmire, high king 568-596, took the Tribute twice without a battle. It was he who invited Saint Colmcille, his father's cousin, to return to Ireland from Scotland to mediate in the dispute between the kings and the poets in the Convention of Drum Cet in 575. Aed's son Domnall was the victor in the 637 Battle of Moira. The death of Aed's son Cummascach was the cause of the central event in the Bórama saga, The Battle of the Pass of Dún Bolg in 596.

It was a custom in those days in Ireland and other countries for local kings to offer their wives as bed companions when the

---

[18] O'Leary, pp. 193 ff.
[19] Mac Airt, *Annals of Inisfallen*, p. 68, n535[1].

high king came to visit. One day, Cummascach announced that he was going to make a prince's royal tour of Ireland and that he expected the wife of every king to spend the night with him. He set off on his tour, sending word to Brandubh, King of Leinster, that he was on his way. We are not told what the other local kings and their wives thought about Cummascach's expectation, but Brandubh and his wife were having no part of it. Brandubh built a guesthouse for the occasion and told his people to tell Cummascach on his arrival that he, Brandubh, was away in Britain collecting tributes.

Cummascach and his group arrived and were accommodated in the guesthouse. Brandubh's servants, with Brandubh himself among them disguised as a slave, prepared a feast for the guests. Cummascach sent for Brandubh's wife and said to her, "Grant me a boon." Knowing well what boon he meant, she said, "Grant me a boon first. Wait until I have finished serving the food, so I can maintain my reputation as a hostess, and then I will come to you." Cummascach granted her that favour, and she escaped to Buchet's House nearby.

Meanwhile, the disguised Brandubh was standing next to the cauldron serving meat with a new three-pronged fleshfork. Glasdam, Cummascach's poet, approached the cauldron to be served first, as was his privilege. Brandubh thrust the fleshfork deep into the cauldron and brought up nine pieces of meat at one stroke.

"That is not the thrust of a slave," Glasdam commented. "That is the thrust of a king." Then he looked into Brandubh's eyes. "And those are not the eyes of a slave. They are the eyes of a king."

Glasdam went to the guesthouse set apart for the visitors and told Cummascach of his suspicions that something was not right. But Brandubh and his men closed the door and locked it and set fires at the four corners of the house.

"Who is burning the house?" shouted Cummascach.

"It is I, Brandubh."

Glasdam said, "Brandubh, you gave me food with your own hand. It is against the rules of hospitality for you to kill me."

This was true, so Brandubh said, "Glasdam, climb up onto the roof and jump down, and we will allow you to go free."

Some say that Cummascach ordered Glasdam to exchange clothes with him, others say that Glasdam did it of his own accord, but in either case, Cummascach jumped over the wall wearing Glasdam's clothes. He fell to the ground and was injured, but he was able to make his way to Church land at Kilranelagh (*Cill Rannairech* – "Church of the Dispenser"), not far from Buchet's House. Lóichín Lonn, who was in charge of the property, recognised him and struck off his head. He took it to Brandubh and showed it to him, and for that reason exemption from taxes forever was granted to Kilranelagh.

Brandubh sent messengers to Aed to give him the news. Aed said, "I have already heard about it. I'll let you go home without harm, but if we come after you, it will be another story." The messengers returned to Brandubh and told him Aed intended to attack Leinster to avenge his son.

The Battle of the Pass of Dún Bolg (596)

The following year, Aed Ainmire gathered his forces and marched into Wicklow as far as Dunboyke south of Hollywood, where he pitched camp. Aidan mac Sedna, Aed's half-brother, was bishop of Glendalough with jurisdiction over Brandubh's territory. Brandubh asked Aidan to go to Aed and request a truce to give Leinster time to gather their warriors. Aidan did so, and Aed replied, "I won't give you a truce until you touch your hand to the three members of your body with which you make babies."

Aidan was incensed at this insult and replied, "May a bitch wolf carry off the three most prized members of your body."

Taking Aidan with them, Aed and his army marched to Belach Dúin Bolg (The Pass of Dún Bolg), the main road leading south to Brandubh's stronghold of Dún Bolg. The upper part of this tri-vallate (three stone walls) hillfort is now known as Brusselstown Ring. The lowest wall encompasses 132 hectares (320 acres) of Spinans Hill to form the largest hillfort in Europe.

"What is the name of this road?" Aed asked Aidan.

"*Belach Dúin Bolg*. The Pass of the Fort of Sacks."[20]

"What sacks are they?"

"The provision sacks of your warriors, which they will leave here tonight when they run away from the battle with Leinster."

They passed on and came to a flagstone.

"What is the name of this grey stone?" Aed asked.

"*Lic Chomairt Chnámh*, or 'the Flag of Bone-smashing'."

"What bones now can they be?"

"It is called that because tonight your bones will be broken on it and your head cut off."

They came into the steep-sided glacial ravine now called Hollywood Glen.

"What might be the name of this gap?"

"*Berna na Sciath*, the Gap of the Shields."

"And what shields are they?"

"The shields of your warriors, when they drop them to flee from Leinster tonight."

Aidan was obviously taking the mickey, but he probably also intended to conceal the fact that at this point on the road, where Aed and his army made camp just south of Hollywood Glen at Kilbaylet, the small round hill forts placed as outposts or "shields" atop the ridges of the Glen, invisible from the road, were now at the invaders' rear.

Aidan went to meet with Brandubh to recommend tactics for the coming battle: "Gather 300 teams of twelve oxen each, and on each of the oxen place two panniers. In each of those panniers conceal a warrior, and put straw on top of the warrior and food on top of the straw. Get 150 unbroken horses and prepare sacks of pebbles to tie to their tails. Set a large candle in a cauldron and use it to lead the whole procession to Aed's camp after dark tonight. Explain that you are going to give the Tribute to Aed, and this feast is a part of it. Since they might not trust your hospitality after what you did to Cummascach, say that you are bringing the feast to them."

---

[20] *Bolg* can mean "belly, bulge, blister, bellows, bag", but it is probably related to the Belgae, a Celtic group, in this case.

While these preparations were under way, Brandubh and his sons and his personal guard chanced upon the young sons of Aed's Ulster allies, including the king of Ulster's son, on a hill above Aed's camp, and they seized them. When the Ulstermen discovered that their sons had been captured, they went to Brandubh.

"Why have you taken our young fellows?" asked the king of Ulster.

"To relieve myself of your grown-up warriors."

"You will be relieved of them forever," the king said. "We will make a truce with you."

Brandubh and the Ulstermen sat down on the hill and agreed a pact of non-aggression. For that, the hill was called Slieve in Chotaigh (Mountain of the Covenant), now known as Church Mountain. Brandubh suggested that the Ulstermen leave Aed's army.

"How can we do that?"

"Pitch your camp in the middle of Aed's camp. They'll object, there will be a fight, and you will have grounds to leave."

This was done, and after a skirmish in which two hundred were killed Ulster stood off and made it clear that they would not take part in the coming battle.

Meanwhile, Aidan was still fuming over Aed's insult. Having had time to work out a comprehensive scenario for the desired fate of one of Aed's three members when the she-wolf finished with it, he came to Brandubh and delivered himself of this rant:

"Great indeed was the dishonour that my mother's son, Aed Ainmire, did to me. The little plant [*lussán* = penis] of Aed Ainmire will be picked up by a raven and taken to Kilcullen. The raven will drop it on the green of Kilcullen, and the schoolboys will use it for a football for seven years. Then there will be a school at Kildare, and the students there will steal it and use it for a football. It will be made into a holy water sprinkler and used in that way for another seven years. Then Maedóc will found the school of Clonmore in Kildare, and a man will steal that holy water sprinkler. And after that, I don't know what will become of it."

Brandubh mounted his horse and went off to seek single combat. Blathach, Aed's champion, who "never threw a spear that

70

missed its mark", advanced to meet Brandubh's challenge mounted on Aed's own horse. Brandubh made short work of him and took his head and Aed's horse as trophies. Aed saw that a battle was imminent, and he said to one of his servants, "Hand me the Cowl of Colmcille."

Aed had once asked his Uí Néill kinsman, the late Saint Colmcille (d. 593), for a gift fitting for a churchman to give to a high king.

"What sort of gift would you like?" asked Colmcille.

"I would like the gift of being always able to defeat the Leinstermen whenever I fight them."

"I can't give you that," said Colmcille, "because my mother was from Leinster. But I will give you my cowl. If you wear it when you are in a battle, you will never be killed under it."

And that is the reason Aed asked his servant to hand him the Cowl. The servant said to another servant, "Hand us the Cowl of Colmcille." The other servant said, "I thought you had it." "No, you were supposed to bring it." When Aed discovered that the Cowl had been left behind, he knew that he would not survive the coming battle.

Aidan's plan was put into operation that night. The procession of ox-drawn carts with their concealed warriors, preceded by the large candle in the cauldron, was challenged by the sentries guarding Aed's camp. When they learned that the Leinstermen were bringing food, they left their posts to join the feast. As soon as the carts reached the centre of the camp, the wild horses with sacks of stones tied to their tails were stampeded. In the midst of the commotion, the Leinstermen leapt out of their panniers and attacked Aed's warriors and scattered them. Aed was killed and beheaded by Rón Cerr, son of the king of Imáil, on the Flag of Bone-smashing, as Aidan had predicted, and is said to be buried in Kilranelagh Graveyard. His widow composed this lament for him:

"There were three beloved sides
By which I'll no longer stay:
Side of Tailtiu, side of Tara –
Dearest was the side of Aed."

71

As a reward for his successful advice, Brandubh gave Aidan Fearna Mór (Ferns) in County Wexford and installed him as bishop. Saint Mo Ling was bishop there a hundred years later. During the next century, six kings took the Tribute, including Aed Ainmire's son Domnall. When the son of Bláthmac, whose other two sons were killed by Maelodrán, tried to take it, Leinster successfully resisted. Bláthmac's nephew Finnachta Fledhach ("Snow White the Festive") reigned from 675 to 695. He took the Tribute twice, but his third attempt was thwarted by Saint Mo Ling.

How Mo Ling Got His Name

He was born to a man named Fáelán and the sister of Fáelán's wife. His mother tried to kill him at birth, but he was protected by a dove and angels surrounding him, whence the name given to him at his christening, Tairchell, which means "Surrounding". Saint Brénainn discovered him, and Brénainn's follower Collanach, who baptized and named him, became his foster father and raised him. Tairchell's teacher was Victor, Saint Patrick's angel.

One day when Tairchell was sixteen, he was travelling alone on a begging circuit to collect food for Brénainn's monastery. His only protection was Collanach's crozier, which he carried as a staff. He was accosted by the Fúath Aingeda ("Evil Spectre"), who was with his wife, servant, hound and nine followers. The Fúath said to his people: "Since I took to robbery and marauding, I never wished to give quarter or protection to anyone except that young man alone."

The Fúath greeted Tairchell cordially: "Where do you come from, master cleric, with your scraps of food?"

Perhaps out of fear, Tairchell replied in an aggressive, unchristian manner: "Where do you come from, dark, singed goblin, to heroic warriors?"

Fúath: "It will be violence enough if I destroy your food wallets."

Tairchell: "You won't unless I let you."

Fúath: "I'll drive this spear through your side."

Tairchell: "I'll hit you with my master's crozier, which has never been defeated in single combat."

Fúath: "It's easier to fight you than boiled flesh."

Tairchell: "I'll pound your hairs back into the holes they grew from."

Fúath: "Prepare to die. We're going to kill you now."

Tairchell: "Grant me a boon."

Fúath: "What boon do you ask?"

Tairchell: "Easy to say. Let me take three steps in the direction of my God."

Fúath: "I'll grant that, since you'll never get away from us. We are as swift as the wild deer, and our hound is as swift as the wind."[21]

With his first step, which was a leap towards the safety of the monastery, Tairchell seemed to them no bigger than a crow on top of a hill. With his second leap, he disappeared from their sight altogether. With his third leap, he landed on the wall of the monastery. When he told his foster father of his adventure, Collanach said, "From now on you will be called Mo Ling from the leaps you have leapt [ro-lingis]."

Timolin (The House of Mo Ling) in County Kildare is named for him, and the ruins of his monastery, Saint Mullins, can be seen on the Barrow in County Carlow. Mo Ling was bishop of Glendalough for a time and bishop of Ferns 691-697.

Mo Ling's Trick on Finnachta: the Remission of the Tribute (693)

Bran Mut, grandson of Saint Kevin's foster son Fáelán and progenitor of the Wicklow O'Byrnes and O'Tooles, was king of Leinster when Finnachta attempted to impose the Tribute for the third time. Bran and the Leinster chiefs went to Mo Ling to ask for his help. Mo Ling in turn asked the old men and historians of

---

[21] I have taken this dialogue almost word for word from Stokes, *St. Moling*, with interpolations from Hyde, op. cit.

Leinster if there was any prophecy or prediction about the removal of the Tribute.

"There is, in truth," they answered: "that it will be removed through a cleric."

"Who knows," said Mo Ling, "that this will not be done by me, and why should I not go and ask for its remission?"

And so he went to Finnachta.

"What is the length of the respite you require?" asked Finnachta.

"A year," said Mo Ling.

"Impossible," said Finnachta.

"Half a year."

"No."

"A quarter of a year."

"No."

"Then will you at least grant a respite until *Lá an Luain*?"

"It shall be granted," said Finnachta, thinking Mo Ling meant the following Monday. Mo Ling immediately bound Finnachta to his promise by the Holy Trinity and the Four Gospels.

Finnachta was not paying close enough attention. "Monday" in Irish is *Luan* or *Dé Luain*. The Irish term for the Day of the Last Judgement is *Lá an Luain*, literally the Day of *the* Monday. The expression comes from the Irish tradition that the End of the World will occur on a Sunday and the Last Judgement on the following day.

Mo Ling had to run for his life when it was drawn to Finnachta's attention that he had remitted the Tribute for all time, but he prayed to Saint Brigit ("bless our path, that on our journey no disaster fall … may we in safety reach our home"),[22] and his fellow saints conjured up a mist that concealed him until he could get out of reach of Finnachta's warriors. However, the Leinstermen held Finnachta to his word – Mo Ling had promised him Heaven if he kept it – and that, according to the Bórama story, brought an end to the imposing of the Cattle Tribute. Mo Ling cursed the king for chasing him, but when Finnachta was killed in battle a short time later, Mo Ling composed this epitaph:

---

[22] O'Grady, *Silva Gadelica*, p. 424.

"'Tis sad for Findachta today to lie in a gory bed.
May he be with the men of heaven for forgiving the
Bórama!"[23]

That is the end of the story proper, but there is more to the
history.

The writers of the Ui Neill, among whom [Saint] Adamnan
[Finnachta's life-long friend, who opposed the remission] is
set down, insisted that the great St. Moling obtained a
remission of this tribute by an equivocation which was
altogether unworthy of a saint, and therefore many subsequent
monarchs of the Ui Neill attempted to compel the
Leinstermen to pay it.[24]

The Battle of Allen (11 December 722)

Murchad, son of Bran Mut, was king of Leinster. Finnachta's
successors, Loingsech son of Aengus (695-704) and Congal son of
Cennmaghir (704-710), had tried but failed to impose the Tribute.
Fergal son of Mael Dúin, high king 710-722, "deemed this
intolerable", and he "ordered a very great and irresistible hosting"
on the northern half of Ireland in preparation for an invasion of
Leinster. Not all the northern half answered the summons. Ulster
was conspicuously absent, possibly because of the non-aggression
pact they had made with Brandubh. And perhaps discouraged
following two recent defeats, those who agreed to go or were
coerced into going seemed reluctant. Each warrior, as he received
his order for the muster, set a seemingly impossible condition: "I'll
go if Donn Bó comes along."

Now Donnbo was a widow's son of the Fera-Ross [near
Carrickmacross, County Monaghan], and he never went away

---

[23] Stokes, "The Bórama", RC 13, 117, 1892.
[24] O'Donovan, *Fragments*, note p. 34.

from his mother's house for one day or one night, and there was not in all Ireland one of fairer countenance, or of better figure, form, or symmetry, than he; there was not in all Erin one more pleasant or entertaining, or one in the world who could repeat more amusing and royal stories, than he; he was the best to harness horses, to set spears, to plait hair, and he was a man of royal intelligence in his countenance: of whom was said – [25]

> Fairest of sons was Donn Bó,
> Sweet the verses from his mouth.
> Noblest of Irish youths:
> All were brightened by his torch.[26]

His mother did not permit Donnbo to go with Fergal, until Mael-mic-Failbhe [an abbot], son of Erannan, son of Criomhthann, successor of Colum Cille, was pledged for his return alive, and until he pledged Colum Cille for himself that Donnbo would return safe to his own house from the province of Leinster.[27]

The armies gathered near the Hill of Allen in County Kildare: 21,000 with Fergal against 9000 Leinstermen. An unsavoury incident is reported in which the Uí Néill warriors abused a local leper, killing and roasting his only cow in front of him and burning his house. He complained to the northern kings, "but the heart of none of them was moved towards him" with the exception of the son of one king, whose life was spared later.

Then Fergal said to Donnbo: "Show amusement for us, O Donnbo, for thou art the best minstrel in Erin at pipes, and trumpets, and harps, at the poems and legends and royal tales of Erin, for on tomorrow morning we shall give battle to the Leinster-men."

---

[25] O'Donovan, *Fragments*, p. 35.
[26] This is my translation from O'Donovan, *Fragments*, p. 34.
[27] O'Donovan, *Fragments*, pp. 35-7.

"No," said Donnbo, "I am not able to amuse thee to-night, and I am not about to exhibit any one of these feats to-night; but wherever thou shalt be tomorrow, if I be alive, I shall show amusement to thee."[28]

The royal clown, Ua Maighleine, was then called on to entertain the host, and he recited the battles and valiant deeds of both sides for the previous thousand years as far back as the burning of Dinn Ríg.

During the battle the following day, all but 7000 were killed on both sides, including Fergal, and "there were nine that flyed in the ayre, as if they were winged fowle, and soe saved their lives", according to the *Annals of Clonmacnoise*. Donn Bó was killed while vainly trying to protect Fergal. Nine thousand northerners and a hundred of their kings were killed, and 180 died of cold and sickness after the battle. No account of Leinster dead is given, which suggests that this is a Leinster account. When Saint Colmcille, protector of the northerners, saw the Leinster patroness, Saint Brigit, hovering over the Leinster army, he withheld his protection. Leinster won. They took Fergal's clown, Ua Maighleine, prisoner and asked him to give a clown's shout, and he did so.

Loud and melodious was that shout, so that the shout of Ua Maighleine has remained with the clowns of Erin from that forth.

Fergal's head was struck off, and the clown's head was struck off. The reverberation of the clown's shout remained in the air for three days and three nights. From which comes [the saying] "the shout of Ua Maighleine chasing the men in the bog".[29]

That night, while the Leinstermen were celebrating their victory with drinking and feasting, Murchad offered a reward to anyone who would go out onto the field of battle and bring back a

---

[28] O'Donovan, *Fragments*, p. 39.
[29] O'Donovan, *Fragments*, p. 43.

77

souvenir. The Munster hero Baethgalach took up the offer. As he came to the part of the battlefield where Fergal's body lay, he and everyone else heard a voice from the sky overhead:

"Ye poets and musicians of the North are all commanded by the King of the Seven Heavens to provide entertainment tonight for your lord, Fergal son of Mael Dúin. Let neither fear nor death prevent you from making music for Fergal."

With that, a chorus broke out from the poets and pipers and trumpeters and harpers, both dead and dying, and never had better music been heard before. Then Baethgalach heard a plaintive chant, an unearthly song sweeter than any in this world. He followed the sound of the melody to where it arose from a bush. He pushed open the branches and saw that the song was coming from the mouth of a severed head.

"Do not come near me," said the head.

"Who are you?" said Baethgalach.

"I am the head of Donn Bó. I promised Fergal last night that I would entertain him tonight. Don't bother me."

"Where is Fergal?" said Baethgalach.

"He is that bright body there on the other side of me," said the head.

"Which should I take away with me, you or Fergal? I would prefer to take yourself."

"Take me," said the head of Donn Bó, "but if you do, may God bless you if you take me to my body."

Baethgalach took the head to the Leinstermen.

"Have you brought us a souvenir?" said Murchad.

"I have," said Baethgalach. "The head of Donn Bó."

"Set it on that post," said Murchad, and the Leinstermen all recognised Donn Bó.

"Amuse us tonight," they said, "as you amused Fergal last night."

"I did not entertain Fergal last night as he asked, but I promised to do so tonight," said the head. "I will sing only if you turn me to the wall, because I sing for Fergal, not for ye."

They turned Donn Bó's head to the wall, and it sang so sadly and sweetly that the entire company was reduced to weeping and lamenting. Then Baethgalach took the head back to its body and fixed it on the neck, and Donn Bó came back to life.

The three wonders of this battle were: the coming of Donnbo home to his house alive, in consequence of the pledged word of Colum Cille, and the shout of the clown Ua Maighleine, which remained three days and three nights in the air, and nine thousand prevailing over twenty-one thousand.[30]

Donn Bó became king of the Fera-Ross in 740 and died in 759. Fergal's son Aed invaded Leinster successfully in 738, and he fought a battle at Kells in 742 with Murchad's son Domnall, which Domnall won. It is not clear whether either of these engagements was related to the Bórama.

Brian Boru

Brian, son of Cinneidigh, is popularly called Brian Boru (*Bóirmhe* in Irish), or Brian of the Tributes. Among the tributes he levied was a renewal of the Cattle Tribute on Leinster in the early 11th century because his brother-in-law, Maelmhórdha, king of Leinster, was aiding the Norsemen. This aid led to increased Norse activity, which resulted in the 1014 Battle of Clontarf and Brian's death.[31]

---

[30] O'Donovan, *Fragments*, p. 47.

[31] "The tribute was, however, revived and again levied by Brian, the son of Cinneidigh, at the beginning of the eleventh century, as a punishment for the adherence of Leinster to the Danish cause: and it was from this circumstance that he obtained the surname of Boroimh, ..." – O'Curry, MS Mat., xi p. 231.

The Saga of Maelodrán

Maelodrán Ua Dimmae Cróin, a prince and warrior-hero of the Dál Messin Corb, was born in the early seventh century about the time his distant cousin, Saint Kevin of Glendalough, died. The Dál Messin Corb, descended from a son of Cú Corb, dominated the rich grasslands of West Wicklow and the borderlands from Naas in County Kildare to the Glen of Imaal near Baltinglass, as well as the kingship of Leinster, until they were supplanted in the fifth century by the Uí Máil, after whom the Glen of Imaal is named. Maelodrán is depicted as a heroic avenger of his people's downfall.

Only two stories of this 9-10th-century Saga are known to survive: "The Tragic Death of the Sons of Diarmait mac Cerbaill" and "The Tragic Death of Maelodrán". They are preserved in the 12th-century Rawlinson B. 502 and later manuscripts. The annals, which are generally factually reliable, record that in AD 651, Dunchadh and Conall, sons of Bláthmac son of Aed Sláine son of Diarmait mac Cerbaill, were killed by Maelodrán. Bláthmac and his brother Diarmait Ruanaid, members of the powerful Uí Néill clan, were joint high kings from 642 to 664. Their nephew Finnachta Fledhach ("The Festive") was the high king who was tricked by Mo Ling into remitting the Bórama.

The saga version of the first story, probably to heighten the dramatic effect, makes Dunchad and Conall out to be the sons of their illustrious great-grandfather, Diarmait mac Cerbaill, whose conflict with Saint Rúadán led to the cursing and abandonment of Tara in the sixth century and who is the subject of a cycle of historical legends. The second part of the first story, in which Maelodrán persuades Diarmait to pardon him, is thought to be pure fiction or migratory folklore.

The Tragic Death of the Sons of Diarmait mac Cerbaill

Dunchadh and Conall, sons of High King Diarmait mac Cerbaill of the Uí Néill line, went into Leinster with a handful of other young warriors to "carry off a *crech*". A crech was a cattle-rustling foray, a form of sport in which young men could test their battle skills and display their courage, and, if they survived, turn a nice profit from the ransom paid for the return of the cattle. However, for the sons of the high king to venture into Leinster at all without a full army was particularly risky, if not foolhardy.

There was bad blood between Leinster and the Uí Néill for several reasons, not the least of which was the fact that what is now North Leinster had been appropriated from the Leinstermen by the Uí Néill and annexed to the royal province of Meath a few centuries earlier. The on-going feud of the Bórama and the recent Battle of the Pass of Dún Bolg in 596, in which the Uí Néill high king Aed Ainmire was killed by the Leinstermen, were other reasons.

Dunchadh and Conall and their companions chanced upon Maelodrán, who happened to be alone and on foot and some distance from his horse, Dubhglais, which was with his horse-servant, Deóraid. Perhaps it was because they thought to cover themselves with glory by killing the Leinster champion when he was at a disadvantage that they attacked immediately, without giving him "fair play": time to prepare for battle and mount his horse. Deóraid was killed as he rode Dubhglais through the host to Maelodrán. Maelodrán called the horse to him, and once he was mounted he was able to turn the tide against his attackers.

He scattered the host and chased Dunchadh and Conall into County Westmeath, where they took refuge in a water mill 10 km northwest of Mullingar by crawling up the sluice and hiding next to the shaft in the understructure housing the turbine. It was a low, thick-walled stone building with a vertical shaft turned by a horizontal wooden-bladed turbine when the sluice-gate was opened to allow the water to rush through the sluice from the mill-pond. When the mill was in operation, all the space in the understructure

was taken up by fast-flowing water and the spinning turbine. It was like a modern food processor. Anyone caught inside when the sluice gate was opened would be simultaneously chopped up, crushed and drowned.

Maelodrán told the old woman in charge of the mill to open the sluice gate. She said, "But those boys will be killed when the water starts the turbine spinning." Maelodrán told her to open it anyway. She did so, and the contemporary poet Ultán described the results:

Red meal the millstones grind.
A king's sons supplied the grist
for the mill of Maelodrán.[32]

---

[32] "This mill was situated on the little river that runs from Lough Owel to Lough Iron, near the point where the river is now crossed by a bridge; and the place still retains the name of Mullenoran [mill of (Mail)oran]. It is curious that a mill existed there from the time of the death of the princes – and no one can tell how long before – down to the end of the eighteenth century; and there are some old people still [1903] living there whose

The boys' father, Diarmait, was understandably furious. He sent word to the Leinstermen that if they surrendered Maelodrán to him, they would be safe from his vengeance. They replied that they would rather die than give him up.

Maelodrán told the Leinstermen that they had nothing to worry about, as he was going to go to Diarmait and surrender. The king had assembled his warriors around his new island-fortress, the *crannóg*[33] at Lagore, near Dunshaughlin in County Meath. Maelodrán went to the lake and watched the boats coming from and going to the crannóg, where Diarmait himself was staying, until after dark. When all was quiet, Maelodrán took a boat and made his way across the water to the crannóg and waited outside the door of the fort.

Soon, Diarmait came out "to bend his knees", or "to sit by himself", as the manuscripts delicately put it. He noticed Maelodrán standing nearby but didn't recognise him in the dark. Perhaps half-asleep or half-drunk or both, he mistook him for one of his household.

"Here, hold my sword and pick me a handful of leaves," Diarmait said. Maelodrán took the sword and handed Diarmait a bunch of nettles and thistles.

"I'm burnt, I'm cut, I'm wounded," cried Diarmait after he had wiped himself with the nettles and thistles. "That was no friend who did that. Who are you?"

"Maelodrán Ua Dimmae Cróin, the one who is just after killing your sons and who is now going to cut off your head."

Maelodrán pulled Diarmait's head back by the hair and held Diarmait's own sword against his throat.

"I am at your mercy," said Diarmait.

"You are, indeed," said Maelodrán. "Let's go into the house and talk."

---

grandfathers saw it in full work" (Joyce, *A Social History* ..., Vol. 2, pp. 333-4).
[33] A fortified man-made island in a lake. See title page engraving for a typical example. The crannóg at Lagore (Lough Gower, a now dried-up lake) was eight feet high and 520 feet in circumference.

They went in and Diarmait explained to his wife, Mumain, what had happened.

"It's a good warrior who spares the life of one he has wounded," she said with a straight face. "We'll repay him by making all our warriors pledge to protect him."

And so it was done. Maelodrán went back to Leinster wearing a fine suit of Diarmait's clothes and a brooch and with two horses with golden bridles as gifts from Diarmait. From that time he fought on Diarmait's side against the Uí Máil.

The Tragic Death of Maelodrán

Maelodrán lived next to the Uí Máil, probably near their northernmost outpost at the tri-vallate earthen fort called the Ring of Sillagh 6 km southeast of Naas, County Kildare, "and his neighbouring was bad for them." He had a fearsome reputation for slaughtering their warriors, and he used to boast, keeping in his enemies' minds the slaying of the sons of Diarmait:

"The Uí Máil are the meal
And I am the mill
That welcomes them all
To their slaughter."

In view of this, although inter-marriage was not uncommon between rival tribes, it may seem surprising that Maelodrán was married to the daughter of Aithechda, king of the Uí Máil. What is not surprising, however, is that one day when Maelodrán's wife was visiting her sick mother, her father asked her to help him and his sons kill Maelodrán. The dutiful daughter entered into the plot with unwifely enthusiasm.

"Very well," she said. "I don't know which of our three cottages we will be spending the night in. You fill my bag with foxfire [phosphorescent rotten wood] – I'll tell Maelodrán it's only my clothes – and I'll walk behind him and drop the foxfire behind me when we go to the cottage, and that way you can follow us."

Aithechda and his sons followed the trail of the foxfire to the cottage where Maelodrán and his wife were staying and surrounded it.

"Maelodrán, are you inside?" the brothers called out.

"I am indeed," Maelodrán answered. "Don't kill your sister. I'll send her out to you."

"She will be welcome," they said.

Maelodrán took his wife's headdress from her and put it on his own head and thus disguised went outside past her father and brothers. They went into the cottage and killed the woman, thinking she was Maelodrán.

"Now see what you've done," he taunted Aithechda as they came out. "You've killed your daughter because of me."

Then Maelodrán attacked and killed Aithechda's sons.

Maelodrán married another woman and made peace with Aithechda. One night he was a guest in Aithechda's house, and while he was having a bath, Aithechda decided to kill him. Maelodrán's servant, Dubchrón, was not with him at the time. One of Aithechda's servants took a panful of hot coals from the fire and threw them into Maelodrán's face. Then Aithechda thrust Maelodrán's own spear into him and killed him. He cut his head off and laid the body and the head on a bed, covering the head with a cloak.

Dubchrón arrived riding Maelodrán's horse, Dubhglais.

"Come inside," they all said.

"I won't," said Dubchrón. "Where is Maelodrán?"

"He's sleeping. Hush! Don't wake him. Dismount and come into the house."

"I don't think he'd be sleeping without me here to watch over him," said Dubchrón. "Take that cloak off his face."

They removed the cloak.

"So, Maelodrán," said Dubchrón, "it's true." And then he said:

> "The face is pale from swordplay.
> Many hands have passed around
> the head of Maelodrán."

85

Aithechda married Maelodrán's widow. A year after the death of Maelodrán, Aithechda was lying on his bed looking at the Spear of Belach Durgein where it lay on its rack.

"It's exactly a year today since I killed Maelodrán with that Spear," he said to his wife.

(The guardian Spear of Belach Durgein is here identified with Maelodrán's own spear. This is discussed in the following chapter.)

"Alas," said the woman. "Don't say such a thing. If anyone in Ireland could come back from the dead to avenge himself, it would be Maelodrán."

Suddenly they saw Maelodrán approaching the Spear.

"There he is," said the woman.

Aithechda leapt up and made for the Spear, but Maelodrán got to it first, and he drove it through Aithechda and killed him. As he turned to leave, he said, "It was not right for you to be boasting about killing someone, Aithechda."

Maelodrán is said to be buried in the graveyard at the Reefert (*Rí Ferta* - "Royal Cemetery") Church in Glendalough, which was established by his cousin, Saint Kevin, as the resting place of the Wicklow kings.

Bronze brooch found at Lagore crannóg.

The Spear of Maelodrán and the Spear of Belach Durgein

Aithechda used Maelodrán's own spear to kill him. Maelodrán's ghost used the Spear of Belach Durgein, which Aithechda had just identified as Maelodrán's spear, to kill Aithechda. Commentators have puzzled over this apparent contradiction and have hazarded guesses as to where the resting place of the Spear was, but no one seems to have wondered *what* the Spear was or believed it actually existed. I think I have found it.

First, who was Durgen, and why was the road (*belach*) named after her?

Durgen was the daughter of Luath son of Lomglúinech and Herccad daughter of Trescu. Herccad was having an affair with a slave, and Durgen found out about it and told her father. Herccad induced her kinsman Indech son of Dea Domnann[34] to meet Durgen at Belach Dá Bend (Road of the Two Peaks, the original name of Belach Durgein) in order to take vengeance on her. Indech tried to seduce Durgen, but she not only rebuffed him, she resisted him with her weapons. Then Indech killed her, but not before she had given him fifty wounds. It is for Durgen's death, about 1800 BC, and life that the road is named.[35]

Where is Belach Durgein?

"Durgen" as a place-name has been obsolete for at least five centuries. It appears three times in 12th-century land grant records as a landmark: near the northernmost seat of the Uí Máil 6 km southeast of Naas, County Kildare; an unidentified place apparently near their southernmost seat in the Glen of Imaal; and

---

[34] A Fomorian king, Indech was the son of the goddess Dea Domnann and Dealbaeth son of Ogma. He was killed in the Second Battle of Moytura, c. 1800 BC.

[35] Condensed and rewritten from Stokes, "Rennes Dindshenchas", p. 324.

as "Dergin" near Glenmalure. It seems reasonable to assume that these "Durgens" refer to a road linking the two Uí Máil centres of power – the two "peaks" of the road's original name, Belach Dá Bend – and extending east to Glenmalure. Old roads rarely disappear completely, and modern roads between the two "peaks" probably follow the route of Belach Durgein.

What is the Spear of Belach Durgein?

The following description of the Spear is inserted into the manuscript where Aithechda is looking at it from his bed.

It would kill thirty bands [700 warriors] with its point and with its front-edge, and by falling to the ground, for it used to be in the road, and a fork under its neck. And whenever any one went past without leaving anything with it, a demon would move it, and it would leap among them and make a slaughter of them.[36]

The Punchestown Standing Stone, in the grounds of the Punchestown Race Course southeast of Naas, is the tallest such stone in Ireland. It weighs nine tons and measures 20 feet (6.5m) from ground level to the tip of its tapering nose. It can obviously kill by falling to the ground, but is it in the right place?

Where is "the guard-place" of the Spear of Belach Durgein?

According to the *Dindshenchas* (The Lore of Places):

Cúldub mac Dein came from the south one November Eve and killed Fidrad Dáime Duibe, for whom Ard Fidraid is named. Glas pursued him until they arrived at the guard-place of the spear made for him through magic, so that it went through Cúldub into the bog. It was not found after that until Maelodrán used it to kill Aithechda king of the Uí Máil after Maelodrán had been dead and buried for a year. So long as that spear was kept concealed and pointing south, Leinster

---

[36] Meyer, *Hibernica Minora*, p. 81.

[controlled by the Uí Máil] was not able to attack Conn's Half [Ireland north of Dublin, controlled by the Uí Néill].[37]

The Spear has to be near the Leinster-Uí Néill border as it was in Maelodrán's time, the seventh century, roughly a line west from Dublin. The northernmost "Durgen" landmark is near this line, as is the large tri-vallate (three earthen walls) fort, partially destroyed by quarrying, called the Ring of Sillagh, between Naas and Ballymore-Eustace. Significantly, there is a clear sight-line from here to the southernmost Uí Máil stronghold, Dún Bolg, the tri-vallate (three stone walls) hillfort now known as Brusselstown Ring 12 miles (21km) directly south. The Ring of Sillagh is a likely site for the northernmost seat of the Uí Máil.

The Spear pointed south against the Leinstermen, so we should look for it just north of the Ring. And there it is, the Punchestown Standing Stone, a mile and a half north of the Ring of Sillagh.

"It used to be in the road, and a fork under its neck. And whenever any one went past without leaving anything with it, a demon would move it, and it would leap among them and make a slaughter of them." How do you wield a 9-ton spear, assuming you don't wish to depend on the demonic possession and propulsion of granite missiles?

For its height, the Punchestown stone – total length 23 feet (7.5m) – has a surprisingly shallow ground-hold of only three feet, its present and presumed original depth. (Compare the 17-foot standing stone in the nearby Long Stone Rath: 21 feet long with a ground-hold of four feet.) The perilous footing of the Punchestown stone caused it to fall in 1931 after leaning for at least forty years. The stone "leans eastward at an angle of 35 degrees from the perpendicular", according to a report in 1899.[38] (In fact, it's evident in the cover photo that even when it is perfectly perpendicular its shape makes it appear to be leaning.) If it had tilted earlier, it might have been propped up "with a fork under its

---

[37] This is my translation based on Greene, op. cit.; Stokes, "Rennes Dindshenchas"; Gwynn, *Metrical Dindshenchas* II; and Meyer, *Hibernica Minora*.
[38] de Burgh, p. 319.

neck", suggesting to a storyteller its potential as a demon-guided missile that could kill 700 warriors at a time "by falling to the ground".

Alternatively, after a few of the socket stones were removed, this stone Spear, concealed among trees, could have been deliberately tipped in readiness and supported by a fork under its neck, which could be quickly jerked out with a rope, toppling the stone onto an unsuspecting troop of invaders. This adds a chilling image to the line "it went *through* Cúldub into the bog". The killing of 700 warriors is obvious exaggeration. One triggering of the booby trap would be enough to impress, even if it killed only a few warriors who were not able to get out of the way in time. The story of a magic spear apparently moved by an unseen force would lose nothing in the telling by shocked survivors.

This scenario need never have actually taken place. As in urban legends, the apparent feasibility of it happening is all that is necessary for the suspension of disbelief. Cúldub may have been its only victim, and perhaps even that story, from the notoriously unreliable *Dindshenchas*, is pure fiction.

How and why did Maelodrán's spear and the Spear of Belach Durgein merge?

I suggest the Stone was appropriated as the Spear of Belach Durgein for a number of purposes: ritual, defensive, propaganda and of course narrative. Standing stones are usually boundary or grave markers or memorials, sometimes combining those functions. There could also be the element of "the custom of warrior bands to erect a pillar stone to commemorate a Rout" mentioned in "Conaire the Great". As they are generally dated to the Bronze Age, and the story of the murder of Durgen is set in that period, it is likely that the Punchestown Standing Stone was a boundary marker to which the Durgen story became attached; or, if the Durgen story has a factual basis, as a memorial to Durgen which came to be accepted as a boundary marker. This leads to the conclusion that Maelodrán, the guardian of the Uí Néill border and arch-enemy of the Uí Máil, had a normal sort of spear, which killed "with its point and with its front-edge", and that his historical and legendary character were grafted onto the boundary marker now known as the Punchestown Standing Stone, which killed also "by falling to the ground", to make it a ritual, mystical guardian. This could be the result of a storyteller's opportunistic borrowing of the Punchestown stone for the Death of Maelodrán story.

Even a minor storyteller, and probably Maelodrán himself, would have been aware of the story of Cúchulainn. The Ulster epic, *Táin Bó Cuailnge* (The Cattle Raid of Cooley), with Cúchulainn recently installed as its super-hero, was committed to writing about the time of Maelodrán's exploits. In several *Táin* and ex-*Táin* incidents, Cúchulainn made unorthodox use of standing stones, uprooting and throwing them and impaling people on them. Scarcely 17 km from the Punchestown Standing Stone, Mac Cécht threw a pillar stone and broke the back of one of the reavers who was making off with Conaire's head. Also, in the Ulster Cycle tale of Mac Dathó's Pig (written down in the ninth or tenth century), Ferloga menaced Conor mac Nessa in much the same way that Maelodrán did Diarmait, and Ferloga went home with a pair of Conor's horses with golden bridles.

It would be an irresistible temptation for a storyteller to combine the local landmark with Cúchulainn's deeds and adapt them both to the tribal hero, Maelodrán. It is possible that Maelodrán's killing of Bláthmac's sons – accepted as fact by the early annalists and as probable fact by most modern commentators – was enhanced and expanded for the glory of Leinster with borrowings from the Ulster tales. Or, of course, vice versa.

Robert Bruce and the Spider
A Scottish Legend in Ireland

After Robert Bruce, King of Scotland 1309-1329, had fought and lost six battles against invasions led by the English kings Edward I and II, he was forced to flee for his life. He sought the security of Ulster, where anti-English sentiment was strong.

According to legend, he was hiding in a cave one day on Rathlin Island, off the North Antrim coast near Ballycastle, idly watching a spider spinning a web, while he pondered whether he should give up trying to oppose the English. As he watched, the spider tried and failed six times to swing from one stone to another to attach a thread, just as Robert had failed six times to prevent the English overrunning his country. Then, on the seventh attempt, the spider was successful. This inspired Robert to gather his warriors together for one more battle, and he defeated the English at Bannockburn in 1314. "Bruce's Cave" is on the northeast corner of Rathlin Island and is so labeled on the 1:50,000 map.

While Robert Bruce is considered a national hero in Scotland, he and his brother, Edward, were not so well received in Ireland. "The Bruce Invasion and Its Aftermath" rates a full chapter in a modern history of medieval Ireland.[39] The purpose of the 1315 invasion was to install Edward as King of Ireland. Robert's purpose was certainly to divert English attention from Scotland, and probably also to forestall any competition from Edward for the Scottish throne. Edward was indeed crowned King of Ireland with the aid of the Ulster lords, but the widespread loss of life and destruction of property and resultant damage to the infrastructure brought on a ten-year period of famine and disease. The unanimous condemnation of the Bruces in the annals is exemplified by this entry in the *Annals of Connacht* at AD 1318:

---

[39] Otway-Ruthven, A. J., *A History of Medieval Ireland*, Barnes & Noble, New York, 1968, 1980

Edward Bruce, he who was the common ruin of the Galls [Anglo-Normans] and Gaels of Ireland, was by the Galls of Ireland killed at Dundalk by dint of fierce fighting. Mac Ruaidri, king of the Hebrides, and Mac Domnaill, king of Argyle, and their Scots were killed with him; and never was there a better deed done for the Irish than this, since the beginning of the world and the banishing of the Fomorians from Ireland. For in this Bruce's time, for three years and a half, falsehood and famine and homicide filled the country, and undoubtedly men ate each other in Ireland.

Edward Bruce was killed in the Battle of Faughart, about two miles north of Dundalk, the scene of many historical and legendary battles over the centuries. His grave can be seen in the churchyard on Faughart Hill, where Saint Brigit founded a church near her birthplace.

The Red Hand of Ulster

This is one of many variants of the legend that explains why a red right hand, palm forward, is the symbol of Ulster.

Two young clan chieftains, an O'Neill and an O'Donnell, wanted control of Rathlin Island. Rather than fight about it, they agreed on a boat race. The first one to lay his hand on the island would be the winner. They set off from Ballycastle, and as they neared the shore of Rathlin, O'Donnell was far enough ahead that it was obvious he would land first and claim ownership of the island.

O'Neill took out his sword, chopped off his right hand, and threw it onto the shore. He won the island.

The Battle Goddess of Clan Turlough

In 1276, a struggle began for supremacy in Thomond (roughly present-day County Clare) between two factions of the O'Brians, Clan Turlough and Clan Brian Rua. The story of this saga, *The Triumphs of Turlough*, was written c. 1369 by the son of the poet who was present at the first of the two battles, in 1317 and 1318, which decided the issue for the following two centuries in favour of Clan Turlough. A legend with ancient mythological roots is attached to the historically accurate accounts of these two battles.

In Irish mythology, Badhbh[40], Macha, and the Mórrígan (Great Queen) form a trinity of battle goddesses. They are members of the Tuatha Dé Danann, the race of supernatural beings who came to be known in later stories as the people of the Sidhe, and eventually as the fairies. The *badhbh* survives in folk tradition as the banshee, who announces and laments the death of a member of one of the old Gaelic families. These battle goddesses frequently appear in mythological stories and legends with supernatural heroes, such as the thoroughly pagan Ulster epic, The Cattle Raid of Cooley, which is set around the time of Christ. During the 1014 Battle of Clontarf, in which Brian Boru broke the power of the Norsemen, a *badhbh catha* (battle goddess) is reported to have hovered over the battlefield, and during a brawl in "The Champion's Portion" the metaphor of a "bright battle-goddess" is used, but that image is a frequent poetic conceit to describe the ferocity of the fighting, and is not meant to be taken literally.

In later historical legends, such as the Leinster saga, The Bórama (Cattle Tribute), a supernatural patron or patroness presiding over a battlefield is normally a Christian saint. What is unusual in the following two stories is that the warriors encountered this mythological character *before* the battles in thoroughly Christian 14th-century Ireland, in the context of straightforward history.

The Battle of Corcomroe, east of Ballyvaughan in the Burren of North Clare, was fought on 15 August 1317 between Donough

---

[40] Rhymes with "hive" or "how", depending on region and era.

of Clan Brian Rua, king of Thomond, and the challenger Murtagh of Clan Turlough. The sides were probably evenly matched at some 9000 each. It is chiefly remembered today as the backdrop to W. B. Yeats's verse play, *The Dreaming of the Bones* (1919), which is set at and near Corcomroe Abbey and its graveyard:

> The little narrow trodden way that runs
> From the white road to the Abbey of Corcomroe
> ...
> [Clan Turlough] and their enemies of Thomond's party
> Mix in a brief dream-battle above their bones; ...
> ...
> ... seven centuries have run
> Since they, weary of life and of men's eyes,
> Flung down their bones in some forgotten place,
> Being accursed.

On the eve of the battle, Murtagh and his Clan Turlough warriors sheltered in the Abbey's buildings while they awaited the enemy, the army of Donough mac Donall mac Brian Rua. Approaching the Abbey from the direction of Ballyvaughan, Donough's men encountered a *badhbh* who arose from the depths of Lough Rask. The following description is a direct translation from the Irish.

Looking over the shining lake they saw a huge hunched miserable monstrous blue-faced green-toothed crone-like spectre with long shaggy hair and a crooked snub nose. The phantom-formed cruel creature had squinting watery eyes, crooked lips, rough-coiled hair like sticks of heather with a pelt of red-grey fox fur that covered without concealing her nakedness. Her narrow furrowed forehead was covered with lumps and running sores and branch-like protuberances. Greedy gaping purple pus-filled bitter boggy beetle eyes peered out through red-rimmed lids under craggy walls of red-grey beetle brows. A great blue-green squashed sprawling snorting piggy snout wide as a fist streamed snot down the sides of the hideous hag. One side of her spacious bulging

95

belching mouth twisted up to her nose and the other down to her bristly beard. The spectre had a pair of rotten teeth like broken wicker and a quick pointed piercing perverting uncouth bitter leprous tongue in her head. A green gristly stripped stook of a stick-like neck supported the head of the hag. Two black-headed round lumpy stony stork shoulders joined her blackened flanks and ribs. Scrawny arms with stiff pointy woodbine elbows and large crooked hands of brutish gnarled twiggy clawed fingers hung from her skinny shoulders. Like two pouchy bags of jiggling porridge were the puny paps on the withered bosom of that heroic hag. A cavernous broad belly spread over her wasted frame. Knobby-kneed, skew-shinned, thick-thighed, ample-arsed, turn-toed, with a feather-flecked evil stream-gap. Two bumpy bare flat feet, bent fingers, crooked curves, narrow black heels, foul fetid fork. That was the appearance of the hag.

She had a heap of heads and arms and legs and battle-spoils which she was washing at the edge of the lake so that the water was flowing with hair and brains.

Donough asked her, "What is your name, who are your people, and who are these dead here on the shore?"

"Bemoaner of the Burren is the name that I bear, of Tuatha Dé Danann descent. Take heed, O king, for your soldiers' heads and your own head will be part of this imminent devastation. Ye wear them now, but they are no longer yours. Ye march now to battle, but soon there will be nothing left of ye except what the birds carry away."

The company was greatly frightened by her bitter prophecy, and they grabbed their spears with a mind to throw them at her, but she rose swiftly above them with the wind and from over their heads declared: "Calamity, tragedy, violence, fierce fighting await ye ..." and she went on to specify which warriors would die and how.

"Pay no heed to that silly creature's prophecy," said Donough to his men, "for she is nothing but a war-goddess woman-friend (*badhbh bancharad*) to Clan Turlough."

All that the *badhbh* prophesied, down to the last detail, came to pass in the battle, which was won by Murtagh of Clan Turlough, who thus became king of Thomond.

In May 1318, the regional Anglo-Norman overlord, Richard de Clare (the name is not related to the county), and his young son set out with a troop of warriors from his stronghold of Bunratty Castle to attack Murtagh, who had been raiding his cattle. As they were about to cross the River Fergus near Quin, they came upon a *badhbh*, probably the same one encountered by Donough the year before, for she is described in the same sort of bombastic and over-cooked language as the previous one. She was washing clothes and armour that looked exactly like those of de Clare's warriors. (This "Washer at the Ford" motif appears frequently in the older stories.) She said to them, "Proud though ye go on your way to the battle, it is a short time till all but a few of ye will meet your doom." Identifying herself as "the Dark Water-doleful" from the Tribe of Hell, she added, "and I invite ye to come with me, for soon we all will be one tribe."

She was speaking Irish, of course, and de Clare asked his interpreter what she said. He replied cryptically, "She makes evil prophecy on this course we run. But for the very reason that we have met her, we should infer that all good luck attends us, because she is merely a well-wisher to Clan Turlough."

Battle was joined at Dysert O'Dea, a thousand warriors on each side. Both de Clare and his son were killed, and a contemporary report states that Richard was cut into tiny pieces out of hatred. As a result of the battle, the Anglo-Normans were driven out of Clare, and Clan Turlough reigned supreme for the next 200 years.

Fionn mac Cumhaill and the Fianna

Finn ... never existed.
T. F. O'Rahilly, *Early Irish History and Mythology*, 1946.

It is quite a mistake to suppose [Fionn mac Cumhaill] to have been a merely mythical character. Much that has been narrated of his exploits is, no doubt, apocryphal enough; but Finn himself is an undoubtedly historical personage; and that he existed about the time at which his appearance is recorded in the annals, is as certain as that Julius Caesar lived and ruled at the time stated on the authority of the Roman historians.
Eugene O'Curry, *Lectures on the Manuscript Materials of Ancient Irish History*, Dublin, 1873.

And whoever should say that Fionn and the Fian never existed, would not be stating truth. For, to prove that the Fian existed we have the three things that prove the truth of every history in the world except the Bible, namely, oral tradition of the ancients, old documents, and antique remains, called in Latin monumenta. For it has been delivered to us from mouth to mouth that Fionn and the Fian existed; and, moreover, there are numerous documents that testify to this.
Geoffrey Keating, *Foras Feasa ar Éirinn* (literally "Foundation of Knowledge on Ireland"), 1634.

The motto of the Fianna was: "Three things we lived by: truth in our hearts, strength in our hands, and fulfilment in our tongues." The last element is the motto of the Rangers, the Irish army's Special Forces: *beart de réir ár mbriathar* – literally "deed according to our word".

The Pursuit of Diarmuid and Gráinne

The earliest known written reference to the Diarmuid and Gráinne tale is in the 9th-century *Amra Coluim Cille*, preserved in the 12-century *Lebor na hUidre* and elsewhere, which quotes the quatrains beginning "Gráinne said: 'I know a man ...'" and "What you have is good, Gráinne." Early names of the story were *The Escape (Ealó)* or *The Elopement (Aithed) of Gráinne Daughter of Cormac with Diarmaid Ó Duibhne*, of which only the titles survive in 10th-century tale lists. The "Pursuit" form familiar today comes from the 15th century through Standish Hayes O'Grady's 1857 translation, but the story was well enough known before then to be alluded to in the 12th-century *Acallamh na Senórach* and poems by the 14th-century wizard-poet Earl Gerald Fitzgerald. The tale is set in the late third century. Fionn mac Cumhaill, "fat and old" in "Éachtach's Revenge", died AD 284.

My main source is O'Grady in *Transactions of the Ossianic Society*, with the Kind Old Woman interlude from Amhlaoibh O Loingsigh's 1910 Irish amalgamation of oral versions gathered from several seanaithe from Cúil Aodha near Ballyvourney, County Cork (see Bibliography – Lloyd).

The Proposal

Fionn mac Cumhaill rose earlier than usual one morning and went to sit alone on the green outside the Noble House, the headquarters of the Fianna on the Hill of Allen. His son, Oisín, and Oisín's cousin Diorraing followed him.

"Why are you up so early, Fionn?" said Oisín.

"I've been without a wife for a year since Maghnais died," said Fionn, "and a man doesn't sleep well without a wife next to him. That's why I'm up so early."

"But why are you without a wife?" said Oisín. "There isn't a woman or wife throughout the length and breadth of Ireland that a man of your stature couldn't have. And besides that, there isn't a daughter of a lord or king that Diorraing and I wouldn't bring to you, by force if not by favour, for you to inspect."

Diorraing said, "I know just the woman for a wife for you, Fionn, if you'd like to go and ask for her."

"Who is she?" said Fionn.

"Gráinne, the daughter of Cormac mac Airt, the High King of Ireland," said Diorraing. "She's the fairest-faced, finest-formed, sweetest-spoken woman in the world."

"The problem," said Fionn, "is that Cormac and I have a long-standing feud, because his grandfather killed my father at the Battle of Cnucha, and it would be awkward if I asked for his daughter and he turned me down. But if you and Oisín asked on my behalf and he refused, it would be easier to take."

So Oisín and Diorraing went to Tara to see Cormac, and when they arrived they discovered that Cormac was engaged in an assembly with the leaders of Meath and Bregia. Guessing that the two Fianna warriors had come on important business, Cormac adjourned the assembly. When they were alone, Oisín explained that they had come to ask Cormac to allow his daughter to marry Fionn.

Cormac said, "There is no son of king, noble, hero or warrior whose offer of marriage my daughter has not rejected, and everyone thinks it's my fault. I'll take you to Gráinne, and you can hear her decision for yourselves so you won't blame me."

They went to the women's sun chamber, and Cormac said to Gráinne, "Here are two of Fionn mac Cumhaill's family, and they've come to ask you to be his wife. What answer would you like me to give them?"

Gráinne replied, "If he's a suitable son-in-law for you, he's a suitable husband for me."

The Wedding Feast

So the wedding was set for a fortnight from then at Tara, and Oisín went back to the Hill of Allen to tell Fionn and the Fianna. Fionn sent word to the seven battalions of the Fianna in all parts of

Ireland and told them to meet him at Tara on the appointed day. Cormac had assembled all the nobles and chiefs of Ireland at Tara, and they gave a hearty welcome to Fionn and the Fianna. They then gathered in the Banqueting Hall to celebrate the occasion with eating and drinking and entertainment. Cormac's wife, Eithne daughter of Cathaer Mór, was seated beside him with Gráinne next to her. Fionn sat on the other side of Cormac, Cairbre Lifechair, Cormac's son, was on the same side of the Hall, Oisín on the other side, and all the others were ranked according to their family and degree of nobility. Daighre Duanach mac Morna, a druid and scholar of the Fianna, sat opposite Gráinne, and in the course of their conversation Gráinne said:

"Why has Fionn mac Cumhaill come here tonight?"

"If you don't know that," said the druid, "it's no wonder if I don't."

"I'd like to have that information from you," said Gráinne.

"Well, then," said the druid. "It's to seek you as a wife for himself that Fionn has come here tonight."

"It seems very odd," said Gráinne, "that Fionn doesn't seek me as a wife for his son, Oisín. It would be more suitable for me to be given to a young man the likes of him than to a man so much older than me."

"Don't say that," said the druid. "If Fionn heard you he wouldn't have anything to do with you, and Oisín wouldn't dare touch you."

"Tell me, then," said Gráinne, "who is that sitting at the right shoulder of Oisín?"

"That's the swift soldierly Goll mac Morna."

"And next to Goll?"

"Oscar, son of Oisín."

"And beside Oscar?"

"Fionn's nephew, Caoilte."

"And beside Caoilte?"

"Mac Lughach, the strong-armed son of one of Fionn's daughters."

"Who is that striking, sweet-spoken man with curling raven locks and rosy red cheeks on the left side of Oisín?"

"Diarmuid the pearly-toothed, fair-faced grandson of Duibhne is that man," said the druid. "He's the most sought-after lover of women and maids in Ireland."

"Who is next to Diarmuid Ó Duibhne?"

"That's Diorraing mac Dobhair Dhámhaigh Ó Baskin, a druid and scholar," said Daighre Duanach.

"It's a fine company," said Gráinne.

With that, she called her maidservant and told her to fetch the jewel-encrusted gold-covered drinking horn that she had left behind in her sun chamber. It was large enough to serve nine times nine men. When the maid had brought it to her, Gráinne said, "Take it to Fionn and tell him to take a drink from it, and tell him it was I who sent it."

The maid took the horn to Fionn, and he drank from it and passed it on to Cormac and fell asleep. Cormac took a drink and passed it to his wife, Eithne, and fell asleep. Eithne took a drink and passed it to Gráinne and fell asleep. Then Gráinne called the maid and said, "Take this horn to Cairbre Lifechair and tell him to drink from it and pass it on to the young nobles around him."

She did that, and the young men all fell asleep as soon as they had drunk from the horn. Only Oisín, Oscar, Diarmuid, Diorraing, Caoilte, and Mac Lughach were left standing. Gráinne approached Oisín and Diarmuid and said to Oisín:

"It's a wonder to me that Fionn mac Cumhaill would seek me for a wife, when a young man like yourself would be more suitable for me than an older man."

"Don't say that, Gráinne," said Oisín. "If Fionn heard what you said, he would refuse to have anything to do with you, and no more would I dare to get involved with you."

"I'm asking you to marry me, Oisín," said Gráinne. "Do you accept?"

"I don't," said Oisín. "I won't have anything to do with a woman who is engaged to Fionn."

Gráinne turned to Diarmuid and said, "Will you marry me, Ó Duibhne?"

"I won't," said Diarmuid. "It wouldn't be right for me to accept a proposal from a woman who is engaged to Fionn, especially since Oisín turned you down."

The Geasa

"Then," said Gráinne, "I put you under geasa[41] of ruin and destruction, Diarmuid Ó Duibhne: the pangs of a woman in childbirth, the face of a drowned man, and the fate of Niall Caille[42] unless you take me away from this house before Fionn and my father wake up."

"Those are wicked geasa you have put me under, woman," said Diarmuid. "Why me and not those other young nobles asleep over there? They're at least as worthy of a wife as I am."

"I have a good reason for putting you under geasa, Diarmuid. One day my father was holding an assembly here at Tara, and Fionn and the Fianna were here, and there was a hurling match between teams led by my brother Cairbre Lifechair and Mac Lughach. The game was going against Mac Lughach, and you knocked the man nearest to you flat on the ground and took his hurley and scored three goals. I was watching from my sun chamber, and I fell in love with you, and since then I have loved no other man."[43]

"It's a wonder that you gave that love to me instead of Fionn," said Diarmuid, "for there is no man in Ireland more worthy of a woman than him. By the way, Gráinne, do you know that

---

[41] A geis (plural – geasa) can be either an injunction or a prohibition, enforced by honour or magic or both.

[42] In 838, Niall Caille ("the Unfortunate") mac Áeda was forced to relinquish the kingship of Tara to Feidlimid mac Crimthainn, bishop-king of Munster, who further humiliated Niall by taking his wife, Gormlaith. Niall recovered the kingship in 841 by defeating Feidlimid in battle, but then drowned in 846 in the River Calann in Armagh. This anachronistic reference in a story set in the third century suggests that the fate of Niall Caille was fresh in the author's mind, supporting a 9th-century date for the composition.

[43] Some say it was because Gráinne saw Diarmuid's love spot that she fell in love with him. See "How Diarmuid Got His Love Spot".

when Fionn stays overnight here, the keys of Tara are in his keeping? That means we can't leave."

"That's not so," said Gráinne. "There's an escape door leading from my sun chamber that we can use."

"It's geis on me to leave any place by an escape door."

"Well," said Gráinne, "I've heard that every hero and warrior can vault over any wall by using his spear shafts. You can follow me that way while I go out the escape door."

Gráinne went through the escape door, and Diarmuid spoke with his friends.

"Oisín, what am I going to do about these geasa she's put me under?"

"You're not responsible for what you do," said Oisín. "I say follow her, but be wary of Fionn's craftiness."

"Oscar, son of Oisín," said Diarmuid, "what do you say I should do?"

"I say follow her, for a man who violates his geasa is doomed."

"What's your advice, Caoilte?"

"Everyone says that I am fortunate in having a worthy and constant wife, but I'd give the world if it had been me Gráinne had fallen in love with."

"What advice do you have for me, Diorraing?"

"I say follow Gráinne, though your death will come of it, and that's a pity."

"Is that your advice also, Mac Lughach?"

"It surely is," said Mac Lughach, "for it wouldn't be decent of you to refuse the daughter of the king of Ireland."

"Is that the advice all of you give me?"

"It is," they all answered.

The Escape

Diarmuid stood up and placed his swift heroic hands on his broad weapons and said farewell to his Fianna comrades. The tears that fell from his eyes were as big as the smooth red cranberries that grow in the bog. Then he went to the upper part of the

104

enclosure and set the shafts of his spears under him and sprang up with a light, dizzy leap over the rampart and landed gracefully on the green outside. Gráinne met him there, and Diarmuid said to her, "This is a dangerous adventure you've started us on, and it would be better for you to take Fionn for a mate than me. Besides, I don't know which way to go."

They set off, and they hadn't gone a mile when Gráinne said, "I'm getting tired, Diarmuid."

"Just at the right time," said Diarmuid. "We can go back now and you can go to your room and lie down, and no one will know we left."

"That's not what I want. Go back to the paddock where the horses of the Fianna are kept and hitch two of them to a chariot and meet me here."

Diarmuid did that, and they drove westward till they reached the Shannon at Athlone. Diarmuid left the chariot there and a horse on either side of the river, and he and Gráinne walked a mile downstream in the water so as to leave no trail and went ashore on the Connacht side. They continued on westward until they arrived at Doire Dá Bhaoth (The Grove of the Two Huts) in Clann Riocaird (Clanricarde) in County Galway. Diarmuid cut down some of the trees and built an enclosure with seven doors, and he made a bed of soft rushes and birch tops in the centre for Gráinne.

The Pursuit Begins

Meanwhile, Fionn had awakened and discovered that Diarmuid and Gráinne were missing. He sent his trackers, the Clan Neamhnainn, after him, and they returned to report that they had lost the trail at Athlone. Fionn threatened to hang them on both sides of the Shannon if they didn't find the fugitives. He sent them back to search for the trail, and he himself set off after the trackers with the rest of the Fianna. When they reported that they had located Diarmuid and Gráinne at Doire Dá Bhaoth, Oisín, Oscar, Caoilte, Diorraing and Mac Lughach were listening.

"We have to warn Diarmuid," said Oisín to the others. "There's Fionn's hound, Bran. She loves Diarmuid as much as she loves Fionn. Tell her to go to Diarmuid in Doire Dá Bhaoth and tell him that Fionn is on his way."

They gave Bran the message, and she understood what she had to do. She hung back in the rear of the company Fionn was leading on the road to Doire Dá Bhaoth, and at the first opportunity she left the group and followed Diarmuid and Gráinne's trail alone to the grove. Diarmuid was asleep when Bran arrived, and he was startled awake when she laid her head on his chest. Diarmuid woke Gráinne and said, "That's Fionn's hound, Bran, come to warn me that Fionn is on his way."

"Take that warning," said Gráinne.

"I will not," said Diarmuid. "Fionn is very likely to catch me some day, and I don't mind if the catching is on the first day."

Fear and fright caught hold of Gráinne on hearing that. Bran left and returned to Fionn's advancing army. When Oisín saw her he said to his companions, "I'm afraid Bran didn't have a chance to go to Diarmuid. We'll have to find another way. Caoilte, where is your servant Fear Goir?"

"Here he is," said Caoilte.

Fear Goir (Shout Man) could make a shout that would be heard across half a county. They told him to give three shouts for Diarmuid to hear. Diarmuid heard the shouts and woke Gráinne and said, "I just heard Fear Goir shout, and he's with Caoilte, and Caoilte is with Fionn. It's a warning that Fionn is on his way."

"Take that warning," said Gráinne.

"I will not," said Diarmuid. "I won't leave this grove till Fionn and the Fianna catch up with me."

Fear and fright caught hold of Gráinne on hearing that.

Fionn and his army arrived at Doire Dá Bhaoth, and he sent his trackers into the grove. They came out to report: "We recognised the track of Diarmuid, and there is a woman with him, but we don't know who she is."

"Bad luck to Diarmuid's friends," said Fionn. "He won't leave there until he compensates me for everything he's done to me."

"It's a sign of jealousy on your part, Fionn," said Oisín, "to be thinking that Diarmuid would be staying around here with no stronghold but Doire Dá Bhaoth and knowing you're coming after him."

Oisín's son Oscar said the same thing. Fionn said, "That won't do you any good. I know you sent Bran to warn Diarmuid, and you had Fear Goil give three warning shouts, but I say again, he won't leave here until he gives me satisfaction."

Then Fionn raised his voice and called out, "Diarmuid Ó Duibhne, which of us is right, myself or Oisín and Oscar?"

"Your instinct is as good as ever, Fionn," said Diarmuid. "I am here."

With that, Diarmuid stood up and gave Gráinne three kisses in full view of Fionn and the Fianna. Fionn burned with jealousy on seeing that, and he swore that he would have Diarmuid's head for those kisses.

Diarmuid's foster father, Aonghus of the Brugh, protector of lovers, never let a night go by that he did not use his powers of divination to watch over Diarmuid from afar. When he saw the difficulty and danger Diarmuid was in, he wrapped himself in a crystal-cold wind and left the Brugh on the Bóinne (Newgrange) and neither stopped nor stayed till he arrived at Doire Dá Bhaoth. Invisible to Fionn and the Fianna, Aonghus went in to Diarmuid and greeted him and said, "What advice has got you into this trouble, grandson of Duibhne?"

"The daughter of the king of Ireland put me under geasa to take her away from Fionn mac Cumhaill and her father," said Diarmuid.

"In that case," said Aonghus, "come each of you under a corner of my cloak and I'll take you away from here without Fionn and the Fianna any the wiser."

"Take Gráinne with you," said Diarmuid, "and if I live through this I'll follow you presently. If I don't survive, take Gráinne back to her father and let him reward or punish her."

Aonghus put Gráinne under a corner of his cloak and they set off unbeknownst to Fionn and the Fianna and arrived in Limerick.

Diarmuid stood up straight as a pillar and put on his armour and picked up his great bladed weapons and approached one of the seven doors of the fort and asked who was on the other side.

107

"No enemy of yours," came the reply. "Oisín and Oscar and Clan Baskin are we. Come out to us and no hurt or harm will be on you."

"I won't come out to you," said Diarmuid, "until I know which door Fionn is behind."

He went to another door and asked who was there.

"Caoilte mac Cronnchon mac Rónáin is here, along with Clan Rónáin. Come out to us and we'll be on your side."

"I won't come out to you," said Diarmuid, "so Fionn won't blame you for helping me."

He went to another door and asked who was there.

"Conán and Clan Morna, enemies of Fionn and friends of yours. Come out to us, and you'll have nothing to fear."

"I won't come out to you," said Diarmuid, "for Fionn would prefer the death of each one of you to my own death."

He went to another door and asked who was there.

"A friend and fellow warrior: Fionn mac Cuadháin son of Murchadh, chief of the Munster Fianna, along with the Munster Fianna, fellow countrymen of yours, Diarmuid Ó Duibhne. We offer our bodies and souls for you."

"I won't come out to you," said Diarmuid, "for I don't want to be the cause of a feud between yourselves and Fionn."

He went to another door and asked who was there.

"Fionn mac Gleóire, chief of the Ulster Fianna, along with the Ulster Fianna. Come out to us, and there will be no bloodshed or battle-wounding for you."

"I won't come out to you," said Diarmuid, "for you and your father are friends of mine, and I wouldn't like there to be hostility between you and Fionn because of me."

He went to another door and asked who was there.

"No one who is here is a friend of yours. We are the Annihilator Clan who tracked you to this place: Little Aodh, Big Aodh, Brave Slim of the Hundred Woundings, Deranged Voice and Aoife his daughter, and Big-bellied Tracker. We are the ones who will cut your head off, and if you come out to us we will make grand gorings on you."

"That's a bad troop indeed, you traitorous trackers," said Diarmuid. "I won't come out to you, not out of fear but because I don't like you."

He went to another door and asked who was at that door.

"No one who is here is a friend of yours," they said. "Here are Fionn mac Cumhaill son of Trénmór of Clan Baskin, together with 400 foreign mercenaries. We are your head-cutters, and if you come out to us we will tear off your limbs and scatter the pieces."

"I give my word," said Diarmuid, "that the door where you are is the very door I will use to leave this grove."

When Fionn heard that, he threatened his men with a painful and lasting death if they let Diarmuid out past them without their noticing. Diarmuid placed the shafts of his two spears under him and made a high dizzy graceful leap to the open space in front of the fort so far from Fionn and his men that they didn't know he had escaped. He looked back and announced that he had gone past them, then he slung his shield on his back and headed west, and it wasn't long before he was out of sight of Fionn and the Fianna.

On the Run

When he saw that no one was following him, he backtracked to the grove and picked up Aonghus and Gráinne's trail, which he followed to Limerick. He found them there in front of a roaring fire roasting a half-boar. Diarmuid greeted them, and the heart nearly leapt out of Gráinne's mouth with joy at his sudden arrival. He told them the story from start to finish, and they ate their dinner, and Diarmuid went to sleep between Aonghus and Gráinne.

Aonghus rose early and said to Diarmuid, "I'm going now, and I'll leave you with this advice: when you're being pursued by Fionn, don't go up a tree with only one trunk; don't hide in a cave with only one entrance; don't go to an island of the sea that has only one channel leading to it; don't eat your meal where you cooked it; don't sleep where you ate your meal; and move in the middle of the night so that you don't wake up where you first went to sleep."

(Each night, for the year and a day that Fionn chased them, Diarmuid built a stone shelter for himself and Gráinne to sleep under. Of these 366 constructions, called Beds of Diarmuid and Gráinne by some people and dolmens by others, about 175 remain scattered around Ireland.)

Aonghus bade them farewell then, and Diarmuid and Gráinne followed the Shannon and then on to Sliabh Luachra and to the River Laune in Kerry. There Diarmuid caught a salmon and cooked it, and he crossed the stream to eat it and then crossed back again to sleep. He had left behind at Doire Dá Bhaoth a roasting spit with a piece of cooked meat without a bite taken out of it, as a sign to Fionn that he and Gráinne had not lain together. Now he left a whole cooked salmon on the bank of the Laune. This was the main reason Fionn would be in such a hurry to catch him.

Diarmuid and Gráinne rose early next morning and headed westward until they arrived at Tralee, where they met a young warrior. He was good-looking and well shaped, but he had no proper weapons or clothes. Diarmuid greeted him and asked him what the story was.

"I am a young warrior looking for a master," he said. "My name is Muadhán. I can serve you during the day and stand guard at night."

"You should retain this man," said Gráinne. "You will not always be without pursuers."

Diarmuid and Muadhán came to an agreement, and they continued on their way until they came to the River Caragh. Muadhán offered to carry them both across. Gráinne said, "It would be too heavy a burden for you to carry both of us," but Muadhán did it without difficulty. He did the same when they reached the River Beigh, and when they had crossed over they went into a cave above Tonn Tóime near Ross Behy. Muadhán made beds of soft rushes and birch tops for Diarmuid and Gráinne at the back of the cave, and then he went into the wood and cut a fishing rod and fastened a line to it, baited a hook with a holly berry and caught three fish. He brought the fish back to the cave and cooked them, and when they were done he said to Diarmuid, "I'll let you divide the fish."

Diarmuid said, "I'd rather you divided it."

110

"Well, then, Gráinne," said Muadhán, "I'll let you divide it."
"I'm happy to let you do it," she said.

"Now," said Muadhán, "if you had divided the fish, Diarmuid, you would have given the largest portion to Gráinne, and so Gráinne can have the largest fish. If Gráinne had divided it, she would have given the largest part to Diarmuid, so Diarmuid can have the second-largest fish, and I'll take the smallest."

When they finished their meal, Diarmuid and Gráinne went to sleep in the back of the cave, and Muadhán stood guard at the mouth. When they awakened in the morning, Diarmuid told Gráinne to keep watch so Muadhán could sleep, and he said he was going to walk around the area.

He climbed to the top of a nearby hill and looked in all directions. He soon spotted a large fleet coming swiftly from the west. They landed at the foot of the hill where the cave was. Nine nines of chieftains came ashore, and Diarmuid went down to greet them and find out what the story was and where they were from.

"We're the Green Warriors from the Channel Islands," they said. "Fionn mac Cumhaill called on us to help him catch an outlaw called Diarmuid Ó Duibhne. There are ten hundred of us, all experienced warriors and each of us capable of fighting a hundred men. We have three venomous hounds that we will set on this outlaw when we find his trail. Fire does not burn them, water does not drown them, and weapons do not wound them. And tell us, now, who are you, and do you have any news of the whereabouts of Diarmuid Ó Duibhne?"

"I saw someone who saw him yesterday," said Diarmuid.

"He'll soon be caught," they said.

"What are your names?" Diarmuid asked.

"Blackfoot, Weakfoot and Strongfoot."

"Have you wine on your ships?"

"We have," they said.

"If you bring out a cask," said Diarmuid, "I'll perform a stunt for you."

They had a large 1000-litre cask brought from a ship, and Diarmuid took it between his hands and drank from it and passed it around, and the foreign warriors drank until it was empty. Then Diarmuid took the cask to the top of the hill and rolled it down

111

with himself on top of it running his feet backwards. He did that three times, and one of the warriors said Diarmuid had never seen a stunt performed if he called that a stunt and that he himself could do it just as well. He took the cask to the top of the hill and stood on it, but Diarmuid gave the cask a kick, and the warrior fell under the cask and it rolled over him and flattened him. Others took up the challenge, and Diarmuid played the same trick on them, until by the end of the day fifty of the warriors had been killed. The rest went back to their ships for the night.

Diarmuid returned to Gráinne and Muadhán in the cave, they had dinner, and Diarmuid and Gráinne slept in the back of the cave with Muadhán keeping watch. Diarmuid did not tell them of his encounter with the foreigners. In the morning he went to meet the Green Warriors of the Channel Islands and asked if they would like to see him perform another stunt. Their leaders said they would prefer to have news of Diarmuid Ó Duibhne.

"I saw someone who saw him today," Diarmuid said.

Then he laid down his weapons and took off his armour and all his clothes except his shirt, and he stood a spear, the Yellow Shaft of Manannán, into the ground with the point upward, and he leapt nimbly above it and slid down the blade until he reached the ground. One of the warriors said, "You've never seen a stunt performed if you call that a stunt."

He put down his weapons and took off his armour and rose bird-lightly above the spear, but he landed heavily and solidly on the point, so that it went up through his heart as he slid down the shaft to the ground. Diarmuid drew the spear out of his body and set it up again, and other warriors tried to perform the feat with the same result, until fifty of them fell by Diarmuid's trick and the leaders told him to take his spear away so that no more would be killed.

The foreigners went to their ships that night, and Diarmuid returned to the cave. They ate the fish that Muadhán caught, and Diarmuid and Gráinne slept in the back of the cave while Muadhán stood guard.

The following morning, Diarmuid cut two forked branches from the wood and took them down to the Green Warriors. He stood the branches upright in the ground and set the Móralltach

(Great Fury), the sword of Manannán that Aonghus had given him, in the forks with the edge of the blade upward. He leapt lightly onto it and measured its length from the hilt along the blade to the point with his bare feet three times, and then jumped to the ground.

"Is there a man among you who can do that stunt?" he asked.

"That's a silly question," one of them said. "There is no stunt done in Ireland that one of us can't do."

He leapt up above the sword, but he came down with one leg on either side of the blade so that he landed in two halves. A second man tried it, but he came down crossways and landed in two pieces. As many of the Green Warriors were killed that day as had fallen in the two previous days, until the leaders told Diarmuid to take the sword away. They asked him if he had any news of Diarmuid Ó Duibhne, and he said he would try to find out something that night.

He went back to the cave, they ate the fish that Muadhán had caught, and Muadhán kept watch while Diarmuid and Gráinne slept. In the morning, Diarmuid told Gráinne that their enemies were nearby, and he told her and Muadhán how he had tricked and killed them the past three days: "They number nearly ten hundred, and they have three venomous hounds to set on me. I think we should leave before they discover that we're here."

So they left the cave and headed back toward Tralee. Gráinne was getting tired by the time they reached Finnliath Bog, and Muadhán carried her on his back until they came to broad and most pleasing Sliabh Luachra. Gráinne and Diarmuid were washing themselves in the river, and she asked him to lend her his dagger to cut her nails.

Meanwhile, Fionn's female messenger, Dear Dhubh (Black Messenger) of Black Mountain caught up with the Green Warriors and asked them, "Who slaughtered your warriors?"

"We don't know who he is," they said, "but he has raven-black hair and rosy-red cheeks, and he was with us for three days."

"Which way did he go?"

"When he left us last night he said he'd bring us word of Diarmuid Ó Duibhne this morning, but he's very late."

"That was Diarmuid Ó Duibhne himself. Get your hounds and set them on his trail."

113

They went to their ships and brought out the hounds and put them on Diarmuid's track. The hounds led them to the cave, and from there to the River Caragh and through Finnliath Bog to Sliabh Luachra. Diarmuid was not aware that they were coming until he saw their soft satin banners adorned with savage beasts. Their three leaders were in front, and behind them what was left of the ten hundred that Diarmuid's tricks hadn't killed. The three venomous hounds that fire couldn't burn, water couldn't drown and weapons couldn't wound were with them, held by chains. A young warrior dressed in solid green was far ahead of the others. When Gráinne saw them coming toward her, she was filled with horror and loathing. She handed Diarmuid's dagger back to him.

"I gather you have no love for that young man in green," said Diarmuid.

"I haven't," she said. "And just now I wish I'd never given my love to anyone."

Diarmuid took the dagger and slipped it into his sheath. Muadhán put Gráinne on his back and they all went a mile along the mountain. Then one of the hounds was set loose on Diarmuid, and Muadhán told him to go on ahead with Gráinne, and he would stop the hound. They went on, and Muadhán took a hound pup out of his belt and set it on the palm of his hand. When the pup saw the venomous hound charging toward him with its mouth open wide, he sprang from Muadhán's palm and leapt down the throat of the hound until he reached its heart and brought it out through its side. Then he leapt back into Muadhán's palm, leaving the hound dead. Muadhán caught up with Diarmuid and Gráinne and put her on his back and they went another mile along the mountain. Another hound was loosed on them.

"It seems," said Diarmuid, "that whatever magical protection is on the bodies of those beasts, the mouth and gullet are not invulnerable. Let's see if I can put the Red Spear of Donn through the innards of this hound that way."

Muadhán and Gráinne stopped to watch Diarmuid cast the spear. He took careful aim and hurled the spear into the hound's mouth, and it went straight through its heart and body until it came out through the navel and pinned the beast to the ground. Diarmuid went to the hound and drew out the spear and returned to Gráinne and Muadhán. The third hound was soon set on them, and Gráinne said, "This is the worst of the hounds, and I'm very afraid of it. Be on your guard, Diarmuid."

The hound reached them quickly. It leapt high over Diarmuid's head and came within a hair of taking Gráinne, but Diarmuid grabbed it by the hind legs and dashed its head against a pillar-stone so that the brains came out through the ears and the broken skull. Then Diarmuid put his finger into the silk throwing-loop of the Red Spear and sent it straight at the young warrior in green who was at the head of the pursuers and killed him. He cast at the second and third men and killed them also. The rest of the Green Warriors, seeing their leaders fallen, turned and fled. Except for those who ran with a hand's breadth between their feet and earth, wood or water, none of them survived but Dear Dhubh, Fionn's female messenger, who flew in a wild frenzy while Diarmuid was killing the foreigners.

Diarmuid and Gráinne and Muadhán carried on with the Shannon on their left hand, and then Muadhán took leave of them, and they were saddened by the loss of his companionship.

"Now," said Diarmuid, "when Fionn and the Fianna hear about the slaughter of the Green Warriors from the Channel Islands they will no doubt be angry. They will be coming after us and they'll catch us and cut off our heads. Do you know that when Fionn chews on his thumb with his tooth of knowledge he will know where we stop?"

"Then fill a bag with sand from the shore, and perhaps Fionn's knowledge won't illuminate him as much as you think."

He filled a bag with sand and hoisted it onto his back.

They headed south, walking quickly until dusk of the night came on them and they arrived at the edge of a wood. Gráinne told Diarmuid that she was exhausted and that they had better stop there until morning. Then Diarmuid threw off the bag of sand and sat down, and he gave a big sigh and said, "I'd rather be at the Noble House of Fionn mac Cumhaill than here tired and hungry." After a short while, he went into the wood and killed a deer and brought it back to Gráinne. Then he built a fire of sticks from the wood, and it wasn't long before the deer was roasted.

They ate their fill of the deer, and then Diarmuid took his sword and cut a pile of rushes to make a bed for Gráinne. He arranged it comfortably next to the stream that ran through the wood, and he said to Gráinne, "This bed is for you. You can sleep in it, and I'll keep watch in case any pursuit is on us."

Then Gráinne went to the bed, and she said to Diarmuid, "There's no reason for you not to come into the bed, for there's no danger to us until daylight."

"I won't come," said Diarmuid. "You can have a sound sleep, and I'll sit here on the bag of sand on the other side of the stream."

The Search

Meanwhile, Dear Dhubh had arrived at where Fionn and the Fianna were, with her legs unsteady, eyes weeping and tongue babbling. When Fionn saw her in that state he asked what the story was. She stammered out the "great, terrible, horrible" news of Diarmuid's slaughter of the Green Warriors and their venomous hounds from which she had barely escaped.

"And which way did Diarmuid go?" asked Fionn.

"I don't know."

Great anger came on Fionn, and he told the Fianna they had to bring Diarmuid's head to him without delay.

"Where are we going to find Diarmuid's head?" Oisín asked.

"Just find it," said Fionn, and he chewed on his thumb until he got the knowledge that Gráinne was lying on rushes and Diarmuid on sand from the shore. When he interpreted this to mean that Diarmuid and Gráinne were not together, the great anger that was on him went away, and he said there was no need to set off on their track until the next day. In the middle of the morning he gathered the seven battalions of the Fianna, and they went along the seashore searching for Diarmuid, but no good came of it for them. As they were searching one day along the south coast of Ireland, Fionn told the rest of the Fianna that there was no way they were going to find them. Then Conán spoke up and said:

"We have searched every bit of the coast, and Diarmuid isn't there, as far as we can tell. Now we ought to go home, but you were saying, Fionn, that it was on rushes that Gráinne was lying, and there are a lot of rushes between here and the Noble House to the north. We should go northward and search the rushes, and who knows but that we might find Gráinne?"

All the Fianna agreed to do this, and they left the coast and headed north for the territory of the Noble House. They thoroughly searched all the rushy places, but they couldn't find Gráinne. Later, Diarmuid and Gráinne placed seaweed on top of a dolmen they were sleeping under, and when Fionn chewed his thumb and discovered they were under seaweed he assumed for a while that they had drowned.

Gráinne's Complaints

At sunrise, Diarmuid called to Gráinne. "You've had a sound sleep," he said. "Now it's time to rise. We'll eat a bit more of the deer and then we'll leave this place." When they had eaten the deer, they started walking again with the bag of sand on Diarmuid's back. At midday, they had to walk through a wet patch, and Gráinne asked Diarmuid to carry her on his back, because she was exhausted. But Diarmuid told her he couldn't do it, "because," he said, "there's already one bag on my back and it's not small."

During the time they had spent together, Diarmuid had no intention of doing anything to harm Gráinne's reputation, for he had great respect for Fionn, although Gráinne often incited him. As they were walking, Gráinne's foot slipped in a puddle, and a splash of water struck her on the leg. Diarmuid looked back when he heard the sound, but Gráinne's leg was already dry. She said, "The splash of water is bolder than Diarmuid," but Diarmuid pretended he didn't hear.

At nightfall they arrived at the place known as Gleann Daimh. Diarmuid arranged a bed of rushes at the side of the glen for Gráinne. "You lie down here," he said, "and I'll make a bed for myself on the other side of the glen." That didn't please Gráinne, because she had no way to get across the glen to Diarmuid. She thought they would both stay on the same side, but it didn't turn

117

out that way, for Diarmuid went across to the other side of the glen, taking with him the bag of sand.

He lay down on the other side in the crevice of a rock with the bag of sand as a cushion under his head. Meanwhile, Fionn mac Cumhaill's men were returning without report or rumour of Diarmuid and Gráinne. Fionn chewed on his thumb again and learned that Diarmuid was sleeping on sand of the shore and Gráinne was on a bed of rushes. Fionn told his people to go again and search more thoroughly along the shore, for Diarmuid was there without their realising it. Then they took all their hounds, and Fionn went with them.

When Gráinne woke up in the morning, she went to the other side of the glen to test Diarmuid, and to complain to him that she was hungry and that he was neglecting her.

"You haven't given me food or drink, and I have a good mind to leave you."

"I told you to do that before we left Tara, but it's no use giving advice to a proud woman. But you won't lack food while you're with me."

The Kind Old Woman

Then Diarmuid headed for the hills to hunt so he could provide something to satisfy Gráinne. But he was unable to raise any animal to kill, and when he was returning to the glen where Gráinne was waiting for him, he met along the path a small woman wrapped in a long ragged cloak that brushed the ground.

She greeted him at once, and she asked him what brought him there. Diarmuid told her what had happened from beginning to end, and that he had failed in his hunt to find something to satisfy Gráinne's hunger. Then the woman said, "Diarmuid Ó Duibhne, I won't allow hunger or thirst to be on you or Gráinne. Come with me to where Gráinne is, for I've a mind to do you both a bit of good."

They walked together to the glen. Then the little woman took off her cloak and spread it on the ground, and every kind of food and drink a person could desire appeared on it. They ate and drank until their hunger was satisfied and their thirst quenched, and then Diarmuid thanked the little woman very much for what she had done for them. He said that he would like to know her name, for perhaps he might be able to something for her in return.

"The Kind Old Woman is my name," she said, "and, Diarmuid Ó Duibhne, I knew your mother, Cróchnad, well. She spent much of her time out in the woods when she was pregnant, for she was going crazy, and she was often at great risk from the wild animals of the woods unless she was watched over."

She said nothing more to them, but she put on her cloak and went swiftly from the place. Diarmuid and Gráinne spent the day happy, and when night came they went to sleep, each in their own bed on either side of the glen.

When Diarmuid woke up in the morning, he called across the glen to Gráinne, and he told her in a loud voice to take his shirt and wash it. Then he stood in the mouth of the crevice where he slept. He took the shirt in his right hand, and he threw it straight at Gráinne's bed. Gráinne rose up and took the shirt and threw it straight back at Diarmuid's bed, and she said it wasn't right for her to wash his shirt. Diarmuid got very angry when he heard that reply. He picked up a pillar stone and threw it across the glen at Gráinne, hoping to kill her. The stone landed close to her but fortunately didn't hit her.

Just then the Kind Old Woman came to Diarmuid and said, "Diarmuid Ó Duibhne, why are you so angry?"

"I have good reason to be angry," said Diarmuid. "I asked Gráinne to wash my shirt. She wouldn't do it, and she said it wasn't right for her to be washing it for me. I don't think I deserved that from Gráinne, because all the time we've been together I've done everything I could for her. I haven't let her go hungry or thirsty, and I let her sleep as long as she wants."

"You have to be gentle with Gráinne," said the Kind Old Woman. "Come with me across the glen to her, and I'll make peace between you. When the peace is made, snatch a kiss from Gráinne."

And it happened just so. They went across the glen to Gráinne. Then the Kind Old Woman spread her cloak on the ground, and there appeared on the cloak every kind of food and

119

drink a person could wish for. She told Diarmuid and Gráinne to sit close together while they ate. They did so, and when the meal was finished the Kind Old Woman made peace between the unhappy couple. Then Diarmuid stole a kiss from Gráinne, and with that the Kind Old Woman took her cloak from the ground and left their sight.

They spent the day together, and it is said that Gráinne washed Diarmuid's shirt for him. But when night came, Diarmuid went to sleep across the glen where his bed was. They stayed a good while there in the glen, and the Kind Old Woman didn't neglect to bring food to them. The storyteller who passed along this story wasn't able to say what else happened or exactly how much time they spent there, but he did say that they didn't get angry with each other again, and when they left Gráinne was pregnant. Several centuries later, a poet imagined what they might have said to each other during that period and put it this way:

> Gráinne said: "I know a man
> on whom I'd forever gaze,
> who brings laughter to my world,
> joy and love and tenderness."

> "What you have is good, Gráinne.
> Better than a kingdom these:
> tender meat of the woodcock
> and a sup of fine smooth mead."

The Wonderful Rowanberries

They went on to Dubhros Ó bhFiachrach in south Galway, where Diarmuid erected a shelter in the middle of the wood after he made hunting arrangements with the Searbhán Lochlannach (Bitter Marauder), who guarded that territory and the wonderful rowan tree that grew there. The Searbhán Lochlannach agreed to allow them to stay on condition that they leave the rowanberries alone.

120

About this time, Fionn and the Fianna saw fifty warriors approaching, and the two foremost were especially prominent for their size and adornment.

"Do you know who those men are?" Fionn asked the Fianna.

"Don't you know who they are?" they said.

"I don't, but they look like enemies."

The strangers came closer and greeted Fionn and his people, and he asked the leaders who they were.

"We are Aonghus mac Art Óg and Aodh mac Anghalach of Clan Morna," they said. "Our fathers fought in the Battle of Cnucha, where your father, Cumhaill, was killed, and were themselves killed in action. We were in the wombs of our mothers, women of the Tuatha Dé Danann, at the time. It is to seek peace that we have come, and to be given our fathers' and our grandfathers' places in the Fianna."

"I would give you that," said Fionn, "if I got the compensation of body-eric from you for my father."

"We have no gold or silver or wealth or worldly possessions, no cows or herds to give you, Fionn."

"Don't seek compensation from them, Fionn," said Oisín. "The death of their fathers is enough compensation for the death of yours."

"It seems to me, Oisín," said Fionn, "that it would be easy to arrange compensation with you if I were killed. I won't accept anyone into the Fianna who does not compensate me for my father."

"What is the compensation you demand, Fionn?" said Aonghus mac Art Óg.

"I only ask for the head of a hero or a fist-full from each of you of the rowanberries of Dubhros Ó bhFiachrach."

"I advise you, sons of Morna," said Oisín, "to go back home and not seek peace from Fionn, because it's not likely that you will be able to give him what he asks. The head he demands belongs to Diarmuid Ó Duibhne, and Diarmuid won't give it up easily."

"What are the berries he demands?" said the Clan Morna.

"Nothing would be more difficult for you to get," said Oisín. "There was a dispute between the two daughters of Manannán over who was the better hurler, Aoife's lover, Mac Lughach of the

121

Fianna, or Áine's lover, Lir of Sídh Fionnachadh. So a hurling match was set up between the Fianna and the Tuatha Dé Danann beside Loch Léin in Kerry. All the great nobles and heroes of the Dananns came to watch, and they brought with them provisions from fertile Tír Tairngire including red nuts, arbutus apples, rowanberries and sweet berries, and as they passed through Dubhros Ó bhFiachrach one of the rowanberries fell to the ground, and a tree grew from it. The berries from that tree have many virtues: no one who eats three berries is sick or unhealthy, there is the merriness of wine and the satisfaction of a feast in them, and anyone who eats one of the berries, if he was a hundred years old he would be thirty again.

"When the Tuatha Dé Danann discovered the wonderful properties of those rowanberries, they set a warrior of their own people to guard the tree, a big-boned, leather-skinned giant called the Searbhán Lochlannach. Fire can't burn him, water can't drown him, and weapons can't wound him. He has one eye in the middle of his forehead. An iron ring runs round his body, and an iron club is attached to the ring. He can only be killed by three blows from that club. He sleeps in the top of the rowan tree at night and stands guard at the foot during the day.

"Those are the berries Fionn has demanded of you, and they won't be easy to get. The Searbhán Lochlannach has made a wasteland of the surrounding district, and none of the Fianna dare hunt there for fear of him."

Aodh said he would rather die seeking the berries than go back home, and so he and Aonghus mac Art Óg set off for Dubhros Ó bhFiachrach. When they arrived at the wood, they found Diarmuid's track and followed it to the shelter he had built. When Diarmuid saw them he quickly placed his hands on his weapons and asked them who they were.

"We are Aonghus mac Art Óg and Aodh mac Anghalach of Clan Morna," they said.

"What is your purpose here?"

"Fionn mac Cumhaill sent us to get your head for him," they said, "if you are Diarmuid Ó Duibhne."

"I am he."

122

"Well, either that or a handful from each of us of the berries that grow on the rowan tree of Dubhros, as eric for the death of his father."

"It won't be easy for you to get either of those things," said Diarmuid, "and the deaths of your fathers should be ample compensation to Fionn for the death of his father."

"What berries are those?" said Gráinne.

Diarmuid explained the properties of the berries and described the Searbhán Lochlannach and how he allowed them to stay there and hunt on condition that they not pick the berries.

"I swear," said she, "that even if the sons of Morna had not come seeking those berries, I will never lie in your bed again until I've had some of them. I'm pregnant, and I won't live if I don't taste those berries."

"Don't make me break the peace with the Searbhán Lochlannach," said Diarmuid. "It's not likely he would let me take them."

"We'll go with you," said the sons of Morna.

"Don't come," said Diarmuid. "If you saw that giant with the full of your eyes it would probably be the death of you."

Diarmuid went to the Searbhán Lochlannach and found him asleep, and he gave him a kick. The giant raised his head and looked at Diarmuid and said, "Is it the peace between us that you wish to break, Ó Duibhne?"

"It's not," said Diarmuid, "but Gráinne daughter of Cormac is heavily pregnant, and she has a craving for the rowanberries, and I've come to ask if I can have a handful of them."

"If you were to have no children except for that birth," said the giant, "and if Cormac mac Airt were to have no descendants but that one, I swear that even if those berries were the only thing that would make sure the child was born successfully, Gráinne would never taste one of them."

"I won't lie to you," said Diarmuid. "I'll have the berries by force if not by favour."

On hearing that, the giant stood up and swung his sword from over his shoulder and struck three great hard blows on Diarmuid so that he made a shambles of his shield. As soon as Diarmuid saw that the giant was off his guard, he dropped his weapons and sprang suddenly on him and grabbed his breastplate with both hands. He lifted him off the ground and whirled him around, then he reached under the breastplate and pulled on the iron band that was around the giant's body until the iron club came into his hands. Then he struck three hard well-aimed blows on the giant so that his brains came out through the gaps in his head and his ears and he was left dead and lifeless.

The two sons of Morna were watching, and when they saw the giant fall they came forward. Diarmuid sat down weak and weary after the combat, and he said to them, "Drag the body into the underbrush so Gráinne doesn't see it, and then go and bring her here."

They hid the body in the woods and covered it over with earth and went to get Gráinne, and when she arrived Diarmuid said to her, "There are the berries you wanted. Help yourself to them."

"I only want the berries that you pick with your own hand," she said.

So Diarmuid stood up and picked the berries for Gráinne and for Aodh and Aonghus, and they ate as much as they wanted until they were full. Then Diarmuid picked as much as the two men could carry and handed them the berries and said, "Sons of Morna, take these to Fionn and tell him that it was you who killed the Searbhán Lochlannach."

"We swear," they said, "that we begrudge him even this much of the berries."

They went to meet Fionn, and Diarmuid and Gráinne climbed to the top of the rowan tree to the bed of the Searbhán Lochlannach, and they found that the berries that grew on the lower branches were bitter compared to those at the top.

The sons of Morna reached Fionn, and he asked them to tell him the story from beginning to end.

"We killed the Searbhán Lochlannach," they said, "and we have brought you the rowanberries of Dubhros Ó bhFiachrach as eric for your father, in hopes that we will get peace from you."

They placed the berries in Fionn's hand, and he sniffed them and said, "These are the berries of Dubhros Ó bhFiachrach, right enough, but I swear it was Diarmuid Ó Duibhne who picked them, because I recognise Diarmuid's scent on them. And I swear it was

124

he who killed the Searbhán Lochlannach. I'm going to see if I can catch him at the tree."

He gathered the seven battalions of the Fianna and headed for Dubhros Ó bhFiachrach, and he followed the track of Diarmuid and Gráinne to the foot of the rowan tree. They found no one on guard there, and they ate some of the berries and enjoyed them. Fionn said that he would rest under the tree because of the heat and because, he said, "I know Diarmuid is in the top of the tree."

"It's a sign of jealousy, Fionn," said Oisín, "that you assume Diarmuid would be trembling in the top of the tree knowing that you're waiting here at the foot."

Fionn called for a fidchell board to be brought to him and said to Oisín, "Let's play a game."

Oisín, Oscar, Mac Lughach and Diorraing sat on one side of the board opposite Fionn. They were playing wisely and cleverly until Fionn was about to win with his next move, and he said, "There is only one move that you can make to avoid losing the game, Oisín, and I challenge anyone on your team to tell you what it is."

Diarmuid was watching the progress of the game from the top of the tree. A skilled player himself, he could see the move that would save the game for Oisín, and he said so only Gráinne could hear, "It's a great pity for you to be in that bind, Oisín, and me not there to advise you."

"It's worse for you," said Gráinne, "to be trapped in the top of the tree surrounded by the seven battalions of the Fianna with instructions to kill you."

Diarmuid plucked a berry and dropped it on the fidchell-piece that Oisín needed to take, and Oisín took that piece, which put the game back the way it was. It wasn't long before Fionn was once again within one move of winning, and Diarmuid saw that and he dropped another berry on the man that should be taken, and Oisín took that man and made the game even. And a third time Oisín was stumped, and Diarmuid dropped a berry to show him the man to take, and that move won the game for him. A cheer went up for Oisín, and Fionn said, "I don't wonder that you won that game, Oisín, with the best efforts of Oscar and the diligence of Diorraing and the skill of Mac Lughach and the direct advice of Diarmuid."

"It's a great envy you have, Fionn," said Oscar, "to assume Diarmuid would be trembling in the top of the tree knowing that you're waiting here at the foot."

"Which of us is right, Ó Duibhne," said Fionn, "myself or Oscar?"

"Your instinct is as good as ever, Fionn," said Diarmuid. "Gráinne and I are here in the bed of the Searbhán Lochlannach."

And with that, Diarmuid grabbed Gráinne and gave her three kisses in full view of Fionn and the Fianna.

"That's no worse," said Fionn, "than the seven battalions of the Fianna and the men of Ireland seeing you take Gráinne from me at Tara, and you being my bodyguard that night, but I'll have your head for those kisses."

Then Fionn stood up with his 400 foreign mercenaries with orders to kill Diarmuid, and Fionn placed them holding hands around the rowan tree, and he ordered them not to let Diarmuid escape. He promised his own weapons and their fathers' and grandfathers' places in the Fianna to anyone of the Fianna who would go up the tree and bring back Diarmuid's head.

Garbh of Sliabh gCua said that Diarmuid's father had killed his father, and he would have revenge on Diarmuid for that. He went up the tree.

Watching from afar, Aonghus of the Brugh saw the danger Diarmuid was in and came to his aid. When Garbh reached the top of the rowan tree, Aonghus put Diarmuid's likeness on him and gave him a kick that sent him down among the Fianna, and Fionn's foreign mercenaries killed him. When he was dead, his own appearance came back on him, and Fionn and the Fianna recognised him.

Then Garbh of Sliabh Crot said that he would avenge his father on Diarmuid, and he went up the tree. Aonghus put the likeness of Diarmuid on him and gave him a kick so that he landed down among the Fianna and was killed like the first one.

Then Garbh of Sliabh Claire said that Diarmuid's father, Donn Ó Donnchadha, had killed his father, and he would have revenge on Diarmuid for it. He went up the tree, and Diarmuid gave him a kick and Aonghus put Diarmuid's likeness on him, and so he was killed. In all, Fionn sent nine Garbhs of the Fianna up

126

the tree, and when the last of them had fallen, Aonghus said that he would take Gráinne to the Brugh. Diarmuid said that if he survived he would follow them, and if Fionn killed him that Gráinne should return to her father at Tara and give their child a good rearing.

Aonghus bade farewell to Diarmuid, and they left unseen by Fionn and the Fianna. Then Diarmuid announced in a loud, clear voice that he was going to go down to Fionn and the Fianna.

"If you had been willing to do that earlier," said Fionn, "we could have finished with this matter long ago."

"It's not to make peace with you that I said I'm coming down," said Diarmuid. "It's that I don't want to leave here without you knowing it."

When he heard that, Fionn placed the seven battalions of the Fianna around the rowan tree, and they tied their shield straps together so that Diarmuid couldn't go between them. When Diarmuid saw them hand in hand around the tree, he put his spear shafts under him and bounded lightly out of the circle over their heads. He then announced to Fionn and the Fianna that he had gone out past them, and he slung his shield over his back and set off. The seven battalions of the Fianna all cast at him together, but he was so far away that none of the spears reached him. He followed the track of Aonghus and Gráinne to the Brugh on the Bóinne and arrived there that night. Gráinne and Aonghus were overjoyed to see him, and they held a feast that lasted till early morning.

Peace

Aonghus rose early the next day and went to see Fionn and the Fianna and to ask Fionn if he would make peace with Diarmuid. Fionn said there was nothing Diarmuid could ask that he would not give him in order to have peace between them. Then Aonghus went to Cormac mac Airt to seek peace between him and Diarmuid, and Cormac said that he would give him peace. Then Aonghus went to Diarmuid and asked him to make peace with Fionn and Cormac. Diarmuid said he would make peace on certain terms.

"What are the terms?" said Aonghus.

"That I be given the barony of Corca Dhuibhne [the Dingle Peninsula], which used to belong to my father, and that Fionn be prohibited from hunting and chasing there, and that it be free from tax or tribute to the king of Ireland. I also want the barony of Djouce Mountain in Leinster[44] from Fionn, because it is the best barony in Ireland, and I want the barony of Céis Chorainn in Sligo from the king of Ireland as his daughter's dowry."

"Will those terms bring peace between you and Fionn and Cormac if you get them?" asked Aonghus.

"It would be easier for me to make peace if I got them," said Diarmuid.

So Aonghus went to Cormac and to Fionn and got all the terms from them. They pardoned Diarmuid for what he had done to them during the time he had been outlawed, and they agreed to keep peace with Diarmuid for a period of sixteen years.

Diarmuid and Gráinne decided to settle at Ráth Ghráinne in the barony of Céis Chorainn in Sligo, because it was far away from Fionn and Cormac. There they raised their sons Eochaid, Donnchad and Aodh, and their daughter Éachtach, whose name means "death-dealing, powerful, extraordinary". We are not told where the sons lived or what they did, but Diarmuid gave the barony of Djouce Mountain in Leinster to Éachtach, and she lived there in luxury with inn-keepers, caterers, young warriors, and people to teach and serve her. They say that there was no man in Ireland wealthier than Diarmuid in gold, silver, cows and cattle herds.

The peace was kept "for a long time", though we are not told how long, but it seems likely to have been a year before the completion of the agreed sixteen years of peace that Gráinne said one day to Diarmuid, "With the number of our relatives and the size of our household and our great wealth, isn't it a shame that the two best men in Ireland, Fionn mac Cumhaill and Cormac mac Airt, have never been invited to our house?"

---

[44] Probably the site of the present-day Powerscourt Estate near Enniskerry, County Wicklow.

"Why do you say that?" said Diarmuid. "They are my enemies."

"I would like to give them a feast so that they will like you better."

"You may do that," said Diarmuid.

"Perhaps it would be better to have two feasts," said Gráinne, "one here and the other at Éachtach's house. I'll send word to Éachtach to prepare a feast for Fionn and the king of Ireland, and who knows but that she might get a suitable husband from it."

They agreed on that, and Gráinne and her daughter worked on arrangements for the two tandem feasts for a year.

The Boar Hunt

At the end of the year, Diarmuid and Gráinne were asleep at Ráth Ghráinne, when Diarmuid heard the baying of a hound in his sleep during the night, and he woke up suddenly. Gráinne caught hold of him and asked him what he had heard.

"I heard the baying of a hound," he said, "and it's strange to be hearing that at night."

"May you keep safe," said Gráinne. "It's the Tuatha Dé Danann doing that because of the protection of Aonghus that's on you. Lie down and pay no attention to it."

Diarmuid lay back down and had not yet fallen asleep when he heard the baying of the hound again. He stood up, and Gráinne held on to him and told him not to go toward the baying of a hound at night. Diarmuid lay down again and fell into a deep sleep, but the baying of the hound woke him a third time. As soon as it was full daylight, he got out of bed and said he was going to go toward the baying of the hound now that the morning was well advanced.

"Then take Manannán's sword the Móralltach with you," she said, "and the Red Spear of Donn."

"I won't," said Diarmuid. "I'll take the Beagalltach (Small Fury) and the Yellow Spear of Skill with me, and my hound Mac an Chuill on a chain."

Diarmuid left Ráth Ghráinne and never stopped or stayed until he reached the top of Beann Ghulban (Ben Bulben in Sligo), where he found Fionn standing alone. Without greeting him, Diarmuid asked Fionn if he was the one who had organised the hunt.

Fionn said he didn't start the hunt, "but," he said, "I came up with a group of people, and one of the hounds hit on the scent of a wild boar and got loose and couldn't be caught. It was the wild boar of Beann Ghulban. It's useless for the Fianna to be chasing after it, for it's often eluded them before, and it's killed fifty of them already this morning. And here comes the boar up the Beann toward us now, and the Fianna fleeing before it. We should leave the hill to it."

Diarmuid said he wouldn't leave the hill through fear of the boar.

"That's not right for you," said Fionn, "for you are under geasa not to hunt the boar."

"What's the reason I was put under those geasa?" said Diarmuid.

"I'll tell you," said Fionn. "One day I was at great broad Allen with the seven battalions of the Fianna, and Bran Beag Ó Buadhacháin came up to me and asked had I forgotten that it was geis on me to be ten nights at Allen without leaving for a night. No other member of the Fianna had that geis but me. So when the rest of the Fianna went inside for the night, I was left alone except for your father and a few scholars and poets and our dogs and hounds. I asked where would we go for the night, and your father, Donn Ó Donnchadha, said that he would give me lodging for the night.

"'You remember,' your father said to me, 'when I was condemned and banished from you and the Fianna, Cróchnad, a woman from the Curragh, bore me a son, and Aonghus of the Brugh took him to raise as his foster son. And then Cróchnad bore a son to Roc mac Diochmharc, Aonghus's steward at the Brugh. Roc asked me to raise and foster his son, Gulban, but I said it wasn't proper for me to foster the son of a servant. My own son, Diarmuid, is with Aonghus, and I haven't seen him for a year. We'll both go to the Brugh and stay there tonight.'"

Fionn continued: "Donn and I went to the house of Aonghus that night, and you were there, Diarmuid, and so were Roc and his son. Aonghus was very fond of you, but his people were more partial to Gulban, which made your father envious. A fight started between two of my hounds, and the women and children ran away from them, while the men tried to separate the hounds. Roc's son tried to escape by going between your father's knees, and your father brought his knees together and squeezed him to death.

"When Roc saw that Gulban was dead, he thought it was my hounds that had killed him, and he came to me and demanded eric. I told him that if he found the marks of the hounds' teeth on the body of the boy I would give eric. When we examined the body, we could find no sign that the hounds had killed him. Then Roc said, 'I put you under geasa of ruin and destruction, Fionn mac Cumhaill: that you suffer the pangs of a woman in childbirth, you have the face of a drowned man, and you endure humiliation unless you tell me who killed my son.'

"They brought me a bucket of water, and I washed my hands and chewed my thumb with my tooth of knowledge, and the truth was revealed to me: that your father had killed Roc's son. I offered Roc eric then, but he rejected it, and I had to tell him that it was your father who had killed his son. Then he said there was only one person in the house who could give eric, and that was your father, for his own son was there. Roc said the only eric he would accept would be that you, Diarmuid, go between his knees, and if you survived he would pardon your father for the death of his son.

"That made Aonghus angry, and he was about to cut off Roc's head, but I stopped him. Then Roc took out a magic wand and struck Gulban with it, which brought him back to life in the form of a singed pig without ears or tail, and he said, 'I put you under geasa that you and Diarmuid Ó Duibhne have the same lifespan, and that he be killed by you.'

"The pig ran out the door, and Aonghus put you under geasa that you were never to go pig-hunting. That pig is the boar of Beann Ghulban, and it is not right for you to wait for it."

"I didn't know about those geasa until now," said Diarmuid, "but I won't leave this hill until he attacks me. Leave Bran with me along with Mac an Chuill."

"I won't leave her," said Fionn, "for the boar has often escaped her."

Fionn turned to leave, and Diarmuid said after him, "I swear that you arranged this hunt to kill me, Fionn, but if it's destined that I get my death here it's no use trying to avoid it."

Death of Diarmuid

The boar came up the hill then, and Diarmuid loosed Mac an Chuill from her chain, but that did him no good, for the hound turned and fled.

Then Diarmuid put his finger into the silk throwing-loop of the Yellow Spear of Skill and took careful aim and cast it straight into the middle of the boar's forehead. But it cut not a bristle of the boar nor wounded it. Then he drew the Beagalltach and struck the boar on the back, but not a bristle was cut, and the sword broke in two.

"Woe to the man who does not heed the advice of a good woman," said Diarmuid, "for Gráinne told me to bring Manannán's Móralltach and the Red Spear of Donn."

Then the boar made a mad, impetuous rush at Diarmuid and took the sod out from under his feet, sending him head over heels. As he got up he found himself straddling the boar facing backwards, and the boar couldn't shake him loose as it ran down the hill. It headed from there to Eas Ruaidh (the Waterfall of Ruadh at Assaroe in Donegal), and when it arrived it took three swift leaps back and forth across the waterfall, but it still could not shake Diarmuid off its back. It then went back the same way and headed up Beann Ghulban again, and when it reached the top it managed to throw Diarmuid off. The boar made a mighty charge and struck Diarmuid so that his entrails and insides spilled out. As it was turning to leave, Diarmuid hurled his broken sword and hit the boar in the navel, so that its entrails and insides came out, and it was left dead and lifeless.

Fionn and the Fianna arrived and saw the signs of approaching death on Diarmuid. Fionn said, "It's a pleasure to see you like that, Diarmuid. What a pity the women of Ireland can't see you now, with your beauty turned to ugliness and your fine figure broken."

"You have the power to heal me, if you wish, Fionn," said Diarmuid, for it was well known that Fionn had the gift of healing.

"How could I heal you?" said Fionn.

"Easily," said Diarmuid, "for you handled the Salmon of Wisdom that was in the River Bóinne, and anyone to whom you give a drink of water from your hands will be cured of any illness."

"You don't deserve to be given that drink from me," said Fionn.

"That's not true," said Diarmuid. "I earned it well the night you and the chiefs and nobles of the Fianna went to a feast at the house of Dearg mac Dionnarthach, and Cormac's son Cairbre Lifechair, the men of Bregia and the men of Meath – all the belligerent powers of Tara – surrounded the house. They raised three great loud shouts around it and set fire to it. You got up, Fionn, and you were about to go out, but I told you to stay inside drinking happily and I would go out and settle with them. Then I went out and killed the fires and made three bloody drives around the building and killed a hundred each time. When I went back inside safe with no bleeding or wounds on me, I saw you laughing and cheerful. You gave me a drink that night, Fionn, and it's more fitting for you to give me a drink now."

"That's not true," said Fionn, "for it's little you deserve a drink or any other favour from me for the night you came to Tara with me and took Gráinne away from me in front of the men of Ireland, and you being my bodyguard that night."

"That's not true," said Diarmuid. "I wasn't responsible for that. Gráinne put geasa on me, and I wouldn't fail my geasa for all the gold in the world. I well deserve a drink from you if you remember the time Míodach mac Colgán gave a feast at the Inn of the Rowan Tree for you. Míodach had an inn on land, the Inn of the Rowan Tree, and another inn on the Shannon, the Inn of the Island, and he gathered the King of the World and the three kings of Inis Tile at the Inn of the Island to make plans to cut off your head. You and a group of the Fianna went to the feast at the Inn of the Rowan Tree, and Míodach placed some soil from Inis Tile under ye so that your feet and hands would be stuck to the ground. When the King of the World heard that you and your people were tied tight, he sent a chief of a company of his people to take your

133

head. This was revealed to you when you chewed your thumb with your tooth of knowledge.

"You saw me coming on my way to the Inn of the Rowan Tree, and you let me know that Míodach mac Colgán and the King of the World and the three kings of Inis Tile were in the Inn of the Island, and some of them were about to cut off your head to give it to the King of the World. When I heard that, I put your body and soul under my protection until sunrise.

"I went to the ford next to the inn to defend it. It wasn't long before the chief of that company of the army of the King of the World arrived, and we fought and I cut off his head and slaughtered his warriors and pursued them to the Inn of the Island. I found the King of the World drinking and feasting with the three kings of Inis Tile. I drew my sword and cut off the head of the King of the World with the first stroke, and I cut off the heads of the other three kings and stuck them on the boss of my shield. I grabbed the jewel-encrusted gold-covered drinking horn full of fine mead that was in front of the King of the World, and I did an edge-feat with the blade of my sword around me. And so as a result of my valour and arms I came to the Inn of the Rowan Tree.

"Then I gave those heads and the drinking horn to you, Fionn, as trophies of their defeat, and I rubbed the blood from the necks of the three kings on yourself and on the Fianna who were stuck to the ground so you could move again. If I had asked you for a drink that night, Fionn, you would have given it to me."

Then Oisín's son Oscar said, "You know, Fionn, that I am kith and kin closer to Diarmuid than to you, and I won't allow you to refuse him a drink."

"I don't know of any well here on the Beann," said Fionn.

"That's not true," said Diarmuid, "for the finest spring of clear water in the world is not more than nine paces from here."

So Fionn went to the spring and got the full of his two hands of the water, but he had not come more than halfway back when he let the water spill from his hands, saying that he couldn't bring it with him.

"I swear you did that on purpose," said Diarmuid.

Fionn went back to the spring, and again when he reached the same point as before he let the water spill from his hands.

"I swear by my weapons," said Oscar, "if you don't bring the water quickly, of the two of us only the stronger will leave this place alive."

With that threat, Fionn went to the spring for the third time and came back with both hands full of water, but before he reached Diarmuid the soul had departed from Diarmuid's body. The Fianna gave three loud cries of mourning for Diarmuid.

Oscar stood up in a violent fit of fierce anger and was about to cut off Fionn's head on the spot, but Oisín stopped him and said, "Son, it is true that he deserves that from you and the Fianna for not helping Diarmuid, but let's not have two griefs in one day. We'll leave this hill now because if Aonghus comes he might not believe that we didn't cause Diarmuid's death, and that not even Fionn is guilty of it."

Fionn and the Fianna left the hill with Fionn leading Mac an Chuill. Oisín, Oscar, Caoilte and Mac Lughach went back and placed their cloaks over Diarmuid, then turned to follow Fionn and the Fianna to Ráth Ghráinne. Gráinne was standing on the battlements of the rath waiting for news of Diarmuid, and when she saw them approaching in that way she said, "If Diarmuid were alive, Mac an Chuill wouldn't be in the hand of Fionn mac Cumhaill coming to this house."

Gráinne was heavily pregnant at that time, and she fell from the wall outside the rath and gave birth to three dead babies. When Oisín saw Gráinne in distress, he sent Fionn and the Fianna away. As they were leaving, Gráinne raised her head and asked Fionn to leave Mac an Chuill with her. Fionn said he wouldn't, and that it wasn't unfitting for him to have that much of Diarmuid's legacy. Oisín took the hound out of Fionn's hand and gave it to Gráinne and then followed the Fianna.

Gráinne's household came out and carried her inside. She sent 300 of her retinue to Beann Ghulban to bring Diarmuid's body back to Ráth Ghráinne. When they arrived they found Aonghus of the Brugh with 300 of his retinue standing around Diarmuid's body. When they recognised Aonghus they reversed their shields as a sign of peace, and both groups raised three mighty cries over Diarmuid's body so that those shouts echoed to the clouds of the sky and the vault of the firmament.

"Never," said Aonghus, "since you came into my fosterage at the Brugh on the Bóinne at the age of nine months, have I let one night pass when I didn't watch over you from afar, except that last night I was not keeping watch and guard against your enemies, Diarmuid, and I grieve for the treachery that Fionn has done to you in return for your peace with him."

Then Aonghus asked Gráinne's people why they had come, and they said Gráinne had sent them to bring Diarmuid's body to Ráth Ghráinne. Aonghus said he would not let them take the body, but that he would take it to the Brugh on the Bóinne, "and though I can't bring him back to life I'll put an airy soul in him so that he can speak with me every day."

Gráinne's people went back to her and told her what Aonghus had said, but she said she had no power over him. Gráinne then sent word to her children, along with Diarmuid's Móralltach and the Red Spear of Donn:

"Arise, children of Diarmuid.
Avenge a good man's murder.
Make strife but do no treason.
May your venture bring plunder."

She sent them to travel the world learning battle skills so that they could avenge themselves on Fionn. When Fionn heard of this, he gathered the Fianna and asked them if they would support him when the children of Diarmuid returned to attack him. Oisín spoke for them all, pointing out that the quarrel had nothing to do with them, that Fionn had brought it on himself through his own treachery, and he alone must reap the results. Fionn then went to Gráinne and coaxed her with sweet words into coming to the headquarters of the Fianna at the Hill of Allen to live with him. When the Fianna saw Fionn and Gráinne together they laughed and mocked them – "Be sure to hold on to her this time, Fionn" – and Gráinne hung her head in shame.

Seven years later, the sons of Diarmuid and Gráinne (no mention is made here of a daughter, but see next chapter) returned from the far reaches of the world, having finished their advanced warrior training. When they discovered that Gráinne had made

136

peace with Fionn, they went to the Hill of Allen and challenged the Fianna to battle. Each of the four killed a hundred of the Fianna, and Fionn asked Gráinne to bring peace between them. Gráinne did this, the reconciliation was sealed with a feast, and Fionn and Gráinne stayed together until they died. If they married, she was Fionn's 33rd wife.

This image from a cross slab at Drumhallagh Lower in County Donegal is believed to represent Fionn sucking on his Thumb of Knowledge, or, as this version of Diarmuid and Gráinne has it, chewing his thumb with his Tooth of Knowledge.
Graphic © Simon Brooks.

Éachtach's Revenge

The place where Diarmuid killed the boar is marked with the Headstone of the Boar, and the nearby grassy mound is Diarmuid's grave, called the Bed of Diarmuid. For two centuries after the death of Fionn and the wasting away of the Fianna following the Battle of Gabhra (AD 284), Fionn's nephew Caoilte lived in a sídh of the Otherworld. When he returned, he went to Beann Ghulban with a group of friends, and he put his weapons on the ground and lay on the grave of his foster brother, comrade and beloved friend. Tears of true sorrow flowed down his cheeks until his face and clothes were wet.

"It is grief to me," he said, "that my foster brother and comrade was taken from me." And they stayed there from midday till evening. Then he said, "It is my grief, my friends, that I would never wish to leave this grave, such is my sorrow and longing for Diarmuid and his children."

"What's that?" said one of his companions. "Did Diarmuid have children?"

"He did," said Caoilte, "and this is what happened when Gráinne told their daughter that her father's death was caused by Fionn."

Éachtach, daughter of Diarmuid,
fiery-cheeked and lithe of limb,
vengeance calls and duty drives
Gráinne's daughter fierce and grim.

Female softness flees the maid
when of Diarmuid's death she learns.
Manly courage – his bequest –
in her valiant breast now burns.

138

Éachtach wakes her brothers three –
Eochaid, Donncha and Aodh.
Rising swiftly they set forth
raging at the break of day.

Fury binds the battle band.
Strong they come to plunder all.
That destruction long was famed.
Great the slaughter by nightfall.

For three days and three full nights
More than on the Táin were slain.
Never was a band more bold
From that time till Judgement Day.

They surrounded Daolgus' fort.
Though Fionn made a valiant stand,
one battalion could not hold
Éachtach and her warrior band.

Fionn called three battalions more
to defend that fort far-famed.
Then the brave heroic lass
set the battlements ablaze.

She attacked with balls of fire
at each corner of the fort,
and she burned Dún Daolgusa
in spite of a hundred score.

Éachtach and her brother-troop
burned and slew from morn to night.
Fionn mac Cumhaill's two thousand men –
all of them were put to flight.

Noble Éachtach challenged them:
single combat maid to man.
Only Fionn, though fat and old,
answered from that rabble band.

Fionn the Fenian chief stepped forth
and a furious fight was seen.
Blow and counterblow were scored.
Slashing swords sang songs on steel.

On Ancient Dripping Hazel
three strong blows brave Éachtach rained.
So hard did she hack the shield
just a red-rimmed sieve remained.

She unsheathed her shimmering blade
brilliant as a gleaming torch.
Daolgus quickly came between
Fionn mac Cumhaill and Éachtach's sword.

When she brought her slashing blade
down on Daolgus slicing through,
such a mighty blow she struck
that one Daolgus now was two.

Éachtach's blue-bright weapon strikes
easily through Fionn's strong shield,
shattering at least three ribs
in the chest of that brave chief.

Wounded, bloody, weak and worn,
Fionn mac Cumhaill, frustrated, groaned.
Ancient Dripping Hazel shield
crashed like thunder to the ground.

Looking like a half-grown lad
in the shadow of his shield,
weeping, beaten by a girl,
fearsome Fionn was forced to yield.

To the rescue of his lord
handsome Ludhorn came not slow.
He killed the courageous maid
with a shameful, murderous blow.

Fionn was ill three years and more
till the healer cured his wounds.
Éachtach lies beneath the floor
of a chapel now in ruins.

This ballad, from the 17th-century *Duanaire Finn (Lays of Fionn)*, Vol. I, was composed between 1250 and 1400. To the best of my knowledge it has never been included in any version of the Diarmuid and Gráinne story, although it supplies a dramatic and satisfying epilogue. Nessa Ní Shéaghdha (*Tóruigheacht*) said: "This is undoubtedly a more fitting ending to the tale and may perhaps have been the original ending."

The history of Fionn's "untouchable" shield, Ancient Dripping Hazel, is recounted in the next chapter. Éachtach's "blue-bright weapon" that shatters the shield may well have been Manannán's Móralltach that Aonghus gave to Diarmuid. The ballad implies that Éachtach was 16 when she fought Fionn immediately after Diarmuid's death, but it is more likely that she went with her brothers on their world travels for seven years to learn warrior skills before that encounter.

Most of the prose introduction is from the 12th-century *Acallamh na Senórach (Conversation of Old Men)*, though I made up the line "and this is what happened ..." to replace Caoilte's list of the names of Diarmuid's six (*sic*: no mention of Éachtach there) sons. My version, shorter than the original, attempts to reflect the style of the Irish.

Fionn's Shield

In The Second Battle of Moytura, the Formorian leader Balor of the Evil Eye, great-grandfather of Fionn mac Cumhaill, was killed by his grandson Lugh, battle leader of the Tuatha Dé Danann. Before he died, Balor told Lugh to cut off his head and put it on his own head, so he could receive a grandfather's blessing and his warrior's prowess. Wisely mistrusting his grandfather, who had tried to kill him at birth because of a prophecy that Balor's grandson would kill him, Lugh placed Balor's head in the fork of a hazel tree, which remained leafless and the home of vultures and ravens for fifty years. During that time, a slow trickle of poisonous milk seeped from the head into the tree, splitting it.

Then Manannán mac Lir, the sea-god and wizard attached to the Tuatha Dé Danann, ordered the tree cut down and a shield made of the wood. Twice nine of the workmen were killed and nine others blinded by the poisonous fumes. The virtues of the shield, Ancient Dripping Hazel (*Sencholl Snidheach*), were that it would be untouched in battle or fray.

Manannán used it in many battles, including the one in which he killed the high king of Asia. Then he gave it to the king of the island of Sigear, for which it was called "the shield of frosty Sigear". It came to the Dagda Mór, chief of the Tuatha Dé Danann, who gave it to his great-grandson Eithear, who became known as Son of Hazel – Mac Cuill. When Mac Cuill was killed in the battle between the Dananns and the Milesians at Tailtiu, the shield was given to Sgoran, King of Armenia, and it stayed with the kings of Armenia for 200 years.

Manannán recovered it, kept it for a while, and eventually gave it to Tadg son of Nuadu. Fionn's father, Cumhaill, took it from Tadg along with Tadg's daughter, Muirne of the Slender Neck, who became Fionn's mother, and on Cumhaill's death Fionn inherited it. In the time of Saint Patrick, the shield was burned by a swineherd in front of Fionn's son, Oisín.

Source: *Duanaire Finn,* Vol. I.

How Diarmuid Got His Love Spot

To be acceptable to the Christian scribes who preserved the story of Diarmuid and Gráinne, the hero must be absolved from blame for his sinful and treasonous actions. This is the reason he is forced under geasa and against his will to elope at the insistence of the wicked temptress. Gráinne is somewhat redeemed by the later addition of the love spot element, so that it is not entirely her fault, either. This is a short version of the allegory – the girl is Youth – in Lady Gregory's *Gods and Fighting Men*.

Fionn's grandson Oscar, Goll mac Morna, and Diarmuid Ó Duibhne were lost one night while out hunting and sought accommodation with an old man and his beautiful granddaughter. They were shown to a room with four beds, and they wondered who the fourth bed was for.

They lay down to sleep, and they saw a light moving down the hallway towards the room, and then they saw the young woman enter the room. The light came from herself, so radiant was her beauty. She lay down in the fourth bed. Goll got up and went to stand beside her.

"Goll," she said, "what are you doing?"

"I thought you might be lonely in this bed all by yourself, and you might want company."

"Ah, Goll, you had me once. You can never have me again. Go back to your bed."

Goll returned to his bed. Oscar got up and went to the young woman's bed.

"Oscar, what are you doing?"

"I thought you might be cold in this bed all by yourself, and you'd want someone to keep you warm."

"Ah, Oscar, you had me once. You can never have me again. Go back to your bed."

And Oscar returned to his bed. Diarmuid got up and went to the woman.

"Diarmuid, what are you doing?"

"I want to sleep with you."

"Ah, Diarmuid, beautiful Diarmuid. You had me once. You can never have me again. But because you're so beautiful and I love you, I'll put a love spot on your forehead. Any woman who sees that spot will fall instantly and completely in love with you."

The Death of Fionn

He was regarded as one of the twelve great poets of Ireland and one of the seven kings of Ireland, who were the high king, the kings of the five provinces, and Fionn as king of the Fianna. He served as captain of the Fianna during the reigns of seven high kings:

Conn Céadcathach AD 123 - 157
Conaire, son of Modha Lamha AD 158 - 166
Art mac Conn AD 166 - 195
Lughaidh mac Con AD 196 - 226
Cormac mac Airt AD 227 - 266
Eochaidh Gondat AD 267
Cairbre Lifechair, son of Cormac mac Airt AD 268 - 284

There are several conflicting accounts of the manner and place of his death. The true story, according to the 10th-century poet Cinaed húa Hartacáin, is that he was killed in the Battle of Gabhra Achaill near Tara, the final battle of the Fianna, in 284. He had already been severely wounded when the five sons of Uirgriu all thrust their spears into him at once.

A popular story says that he had been deserted by all but one member of the Fianna because they considered him too old to lead them. He went to Áth Brea on the River Boyne where he used to test his physical abilities once a year by leaping across the stream. But this time he slipped and fell between two rocks, striking his head fatally.

Four fishermen found his body – the three sons of Uirgriu and Aiclech mac Dubdriu. Aiclech cut off his head, and the sons of Uirgriu killed Aiclech and took Fionn's head with them into an empty house. They set the head next to the fire while they cooked their fish. One of the men joked: "Give a piece to the head, since Aiclech is dead." They divided the fish into two portions, but when they did there were suddenly three portions. Three times they divided it into two portions, but still there were three.

"How did that happen?" said one of them.

Fionn's head answered: "The reason you keep getting three portions is that one of them is supposed to be for me."

Fionn's nephew Caoilte killed the sons of Uirgriu in revenge.

A persistent tradition in both Ireland and Scotland, where he is known as Fingal,[45] has it that Fionn, like Earl Gerald and Red Hugh O'Donnell, lies sleeping in a cave with members of the Fianna and the Trumpet of the Fianna. Some day, a man will stumble upon the cave and blow three blasts on the Trumpet, and Fionn and the Fianna will awake and rise again as strong as ever.

---

[45] "It has been the fate of this popular Irish hero, after a long course of traditional renown in his country – where his name still lives, not only in legends and songs, but yet in the most indelible records of scenery connected with his memory – to have been all at once transferred, *by adoption*, to another country [Scotland], and start under a new but false shape, in a fresh career of fame." Thomas Moore, *History of Ireland*.

Caoilte Laments the Passing of the Fianna

In this extract from the 15-16th-century 106-stanza "Lay of Beann Ghualann" from the 17th-century *Duanaire Finn*, Vol. II, Fionn's nephew Caoilte has met with Saint Patrick, who is trying to convert him to Christianity. Caoilte speaks first.

"Pitiful this piety
and lamenting Baskin Clan.
If I had my health of yore
piety I soon would ban."

"Say not so, Caoilte, my friend.
If you knew of heaven's grace
never would you miss or mourn
comrades of the Fenian race."

"If you knew the Fenian chief
and the gallant Ulster youth,
hunching in their hunting hides,
piety would not please you."

"Bad the reasoning, old man.
All that mighty host will fall.
Not a single one escapes
judgement of the King of All."

"O Patrick, saint of Ireland,
sad to see those heroes bold
taken from me and the world,
leaving me bereft alone."

Notes on the Stories

Conaire the Great

At the bottom of folio 83 of *Lebor na hUidre*, where Conaire lists the gifts he gave to Dá Derga, a later hand than that of the scribe who wrote the text, presumably belonging to a man also named Conaire, has inserted this "there but for the grace of God" comment: "Ten sparkles in a black bag, not a profound or fine gleaming gift. Although my namesake is doomed, my choice of heaven shines."

The Bórama

Tuathal Techmar

Dáithí Ó hÓgáin says that "Tuathal" is "the Irish version of a postulated Celtic 'Teutovalos', meaning 'people's leader'".[46] "Techmar" is alternatively derived from "legitimate", for his being of the royal line, and "acquisitive", because of his appropriation – *techtadh* – of the heads of his defeated enemies. *Lebor Gabála* (*The Book of Occupations*) says it is from *techt tar muir* – "coming over-sea".[47]

Romans in Ireland?

Apart from Robert Fabyan's cryptic comment in his 1516 *The New Chronicles of England and France* – "Claudius sent certayne Legions of his knyghtes into Irlande to rule that Countrie" – there is no historical, literary, legendary or archaeological evidence that

---

[46] Ó hÓgáin, *Myth, Legend*, p. 409.
[47] Macalister, *Lebor Gabála Érenn* Part IV, p. 311.

the Romans ever established a military presence in Ireland. However, it is suspected that Tuathal's swift conquest of Ireland may have been in some way aided by the Romans – perhaps with "advisors", training, arms – in whose interest it was for Ireland to be dominated by a strong ruler who owed them a favour. Agricola was governor of Britain (AD 77 - 85) at the time Tuathal Techmar was active. Agricola's son-in-law and devoted biographer, Tacitus, said, "Agricola had given shelter to one of the [Irish] petty chieftains whom faction had driven from home, and under the cloak of friendship held him in reserve to be used as opportunity offered" (*Agricola 24*). This is believed to be Tuathal, who as a return favour to Agricola may have agreed not to invade Roman Britain. If Agricola had actually invaded Ireland, the hero-worshipping Tacitus would have said so, which he did not.

Ráth Imáil

No one has identified the site of this rath, but Crossoona (pronounced "crish-OO-na") Rath, a ringfort 65m in diameter on the southeast slope of Kilranelagh Hill, would be a good candidate. It is open to the south and sheltered by Kilranelagh Hill on the west, Keadeen Mountain on the east, and Spinans Hill (Dún Bolg) to the north. The rebel leader Michael Dwyer used Crossoona Rath during a running skirmish with British troops in early September 1798.

The *Claenfherta* (Sloping Trenches) of Tara

The false judgement by the usurper high king Lugaid mac Con is also given as the cause of the slipping of the mounds. Lugaid said that a widow should give her sheep to a man whose pasture they had grazed. Ten-year-old Cormac mac Airt disagreed, saying a shearing should compensate for a shearing; that is, the owner of the pasture should be given one season's shearing of the sheep as ample compensation. The people agreed, Lugaid was forced to reverse his decision, and the judgement passed into law and was cited as case law in some parts of Ireland until the early 20th century.

The Death of Cummascach (595)

Killing guests by setting fire to the guesthouse is a universal motif found elsewhere in Irish tradition. The Leinster king Labhraidh Loingsigh did the same thing to his great-uncle, High King Cobhtach Caol, to avenge the murders of his father and grandfather in the third century BC at Dinn Ríg in County Carlow. This is one of the famous "king-stories" told to the Uí Néill army by the royal fool the night before the Battle of Allen (AD 722), and Brandubh would surely have been familiar with it. So, for that matter, would Glasdam and Cummascach.

> Labhraidh Loingsigh full of grief
> slew King Cobhtach in Dinn Ríg.
> Lance-men [*láignech*] from across the waves
> gave the Leinstermen [*Laighean*] their name.[48]

Buchet's House

Evidence in the Bórama saga indicates that Buchet's House, where Brandubh's wife sought refuge from Cummascach, was located at or near the present Kilranelagh House on Kilranelagh Hill near Baltinglass. Liam Price agreed with this siting and added that the green of *Cill Rannairech* (Ranelagh Church), where Cummascach was killed, was also in the vicinity: "All the Annals contain the statement that Cummascach was killed at Dun Buchat."[49]

Dún Bolg

The three concentric stone walls of Brusselstown Ring on Spinans Hill near Baltinglass constitute the largest hillfort in Europe at 132 hectares, known to legend and history as Dún Bolg, for which is named the central incident in the Bórama saga, the

---

[48] My translation of the Irish in Gwynn, *Metrical Dindshenchas* II, p. 52.
[49] Price, *Place-names*, p. 121.

Battle of the Pass of Dún Bolg – "one of the most important in early Irish history"[50] because it halted the expansion of the Uí Néill.

Saint Colmcille

Saint Colmcille (520-593) was a prince of the royal Uí Néill line, poet and Christianised druid. He copied a psalter written out by Saint Finnen. When he returned the original, Finnen demanded the copy. Colmcille refused, saying the copy belonged to him. The case went to High King Diarmait mac Cerbaill, the "father" (actually great-grandfather) of the princes killed by Maelodrán, who gave a famous judgement, the first copyright law in Ireland: "To every cow its calf, and to every book its copy." When Diarmait killed the son of the king of Connacht, who was under Colmcille's protection, in 560, Colmcille instigated a civil war, the Battle of Cul-Dreimhne (near Sligo), in which Aed Ainmire's father fought on Colmcille's side. (They were cousins.) Three thousand of Diarmait's warriors were killed, but only one of Colmcille's men was killed, and that was only because he had strayed beyond the physical limit of Colmcille's protection.

His protection was sought by the Uí Néill even after his death, as in the 722 Battle of Allen. The O'Donnells, a sept of the Uí Néill, acquired Colmcille's psalter, and as "The *Cathach*" (Battler) it was carried by them into battle until the 16th century. It is now preserved in the Royal Irish Academy in Dublin, where it is displayed on special occasions.

Saint Brigit, now mainly associated with Kildare, was the patroness of the Leinster warriors.

"Nine that flyed in the ayre, as if they were winged fowle"

Conell Mageoghagan's picturesque translation in his *Annals of Clonmacnoise* (1627) cannot be checked, as the Irish original has gone missing. The *Annals of the Four Masters* (AFM),

---

[50] Walshe, p. 118.

transcribed between 1632 and 1636, have at AD 718 [*recte* 722]: *"Naonbhar tra issídh lotar hi faindeal ocus ngealtacht as in cath sin."* If AFM's source is the same as the text Mageoghagan worked from, he may have taken *hi faindeal* for "feathered" (*faind* = "plumage, feathers" – *Dictionary of the Irish Language* [DIL]). DIL does not have *faindeal*, but the word is probably based on *fann* = "weak". This is the general sense taken by other editors. O'Donovan (*Fragments*) says that nine ran panicked and mad from the battle.

The Saga of Maelodrán

The poet who described the death of the king's sons in the water mill was Saint Ultán Mac-Ui-Conchobair, bishop at Ardbraccan near Navan in County Meath, who died in 656. He co-authored the Tripartite Life of Saint Patrick and wrote a number of hymns and poems to Saint Brigit, to whom he was related, and probably wrote her Third Life. His feast day is 4 September.

The Triumphs of Turlough

Seán Mac Ruaidhrí Mac Craith, author of *The Triumphs of Turlough* (*Caithréim Thoirdhealbhaigh*), was the son of clan poet Ruaidhrí Mac Craith, who exhorted the warriors in the elaborate style typical of the era: "Under Ruaidhrí Mac Craith, Clancraith with enunciation of their choicest counsels edified the gentles, saying that this enterprise surely was one to undertake without scruple ... Since in poesy Clancraith excel all others, by and bye upon the way publicly they will recite it all" (O'Grady, *Caithréim*). Seán Mac Ruaidhrí employed some 54,000 words to tell the story, many of them invented compounds that don't otherwise exist. As an example, here is the end of the description of the hag: "lethantrosdán lomdeilecha lúbméracha laobgloithnecha lebar-sálgorma liathgormingnecha ladharbrénfliucha lanntrusgacha."

The Battle Goddess of Clan Turlough

This story survives as a local legend, inspiring American musician Danny Carnahan to write a song called "Loughrask". He says in a liner note on his 1989 CD *Journeys of the Heart*: "Several years ago I was told a story in Ballyvaughan, Co. Clare, about a 1000-year-old legend of the 'Hag of Loughrask'."

In personal correspondence, he expanded: "In 1978 or 1979, I met Bernie and Doreen Comyn of Loughrask House, just outside Ballyvaughan at the edge of Loughrask. Bernie told me the legend of the Hag of Loughrask, as he had had it from his father and on back some 400 years that their family had lived in the area. I included pretty much everything that he told me in the song. That's about the extent of my knowledge of the legend. Bernie indicated that the Hag had appeared twice more in the following centuries, but he didn't know when or who might have witnessed it."

Here are the relevant lines from the song (O'Loughlainn was one of the slain battle leaders):

And we stopped where Loughrask lay so peaceful and wide
And a cry echoed over the water

And the grey hag she rose where no foothold could be
From the heart of the lake, with her back to the sea
And she thrust out her hand as her eyes turned to me
Saying, Soldier of Loughlainn, take warning

Get you home, Lord O'Loughlainn, return while you may
For your fate is decreed if you march on your way
And no man may fight with you and live out the day
And a cold wind will blow on the Burren

O'Loughlainn just smiled as he raised up his hand
I hark not to vision nor bow to demand
And there's no one on earth, be he devil or man
Can lure me to faithless surrender

© Copyright 1984 Danny Carnahan/Post-Trad Music

Bibliography

Annals of Clonmacnoise, from the Creation to 1408 A.D., The, trans. 1627 by Conell Mageoghagan, ed. Rev. Denis Murphy, S. J., Royal Society of Antiquaries of Ireland, Dublin, 1896.

Annals of Ireland, see O'Donovan, John, *Annals of Ireland.*

Best, R. I. and Osborn Bergin, *Lebor na hUidre: Book of the Dun Cow,* Royal Irish Academy, Dublin, 1929.

Byrne, Francis John, *Irish Kings and High-kings,* London, 1973; 2001.

Chronicum [also *Chronicon*] *Scotorum: A Chronicle of Irish Affairs from the Earliest Times to AD 1135,* by D. MacFirbisigh, ed/trans. William M. Hennessy; Longmanns, 1866.

de Burgh, T. J., "Ancient Naas: Outposts and Longstones", JKAS 2, 1899.

Dictionary of the Irish Language Based Mainly on Old and Middle Irish Materials, Compact Edition, Royal Irish Academy, Dublin, 1983; eDIL.

Dillon, Myles, *The Cycles of the Kings,* Oxford, 1946, reprinted by Four Courts Press, Dublin, 1994.

Dinneen, Patrick, *Foclóir Gaedhilge agus Béarla: an Irish-English Dictionary,* Irish Texts Society, Dublin, 1927.

Dooley, Ann and Harry Roe, *Tales of the Elders of Ireland,* Oxford, 1999. (This is a translation of *Acallam na Senórach.*)

Fragments, see O'Donovan, John, *Annals of Ireland: Three Fragments ...*

Greene, David, *Fingal Rónáin and Other Stories,* School of Celtic Studies, Dublin Institute for Advanced Studies, Mediaeval and Modern Irish Series, Vol xvi; 1955.

Gregory, Lady Augusta, *Gods and Fighting Men,* John Murray, 1904; Colin Smythe, 1970.

Gwynn, Edward J., *The Metrical Dindshenchas,* Royal Irish Academy, Dublin, 1903-1935. Reprinted 1991 by the School of Celtic Studies, Dublin Institute for Advanced Studies.

Hannigan, Ken and William Nolan, eds., *Wicklow History and Society: Interdisciplinary Essays on the History of an Irish County*, Geography Publications, Dublin, 1994.

Hencken, H. O'Neill, "Lagore Crannóg", PRIA liii, C, 32, 1950.

Henderson, George, *Fled Bricrend* (The Feast of Bricriu), Irish Texts Society, 1899.

Hogan, Edmund, *Onomasticon Goedelicum Locorum et Tribum Hiberniae et Scotiae: An Index, with Identifications, to the Gaelic Names of Places and Tribes*, Hodges, Figgis & Co., Dublin; Williams & Norgate, London, 1910.

Holweck, F. G., *A Biographical Dictionary of the Saints*, Herder, St Louis USA, 1924.

Hyde, Douglas, *Legends of Saints and Sinners*, Talbot Press, Dublin, no date.

Joyce, P. W., *A Social History of Ancient Ireland*, Gresham, Dublin & Belfast, 1903.

Joyce, P. W., *The Origin and History of Irish Names of Places*, Dublin, London, 1869.

Leask, H. G., "The Long Stone, Punchestown, Co. Kildare", JRSAI, Vol. 67, 1937.

Lloyd, J. H., "Diarmuid and Gráinne as a Folk-tale", *Gadelica: A Journal of Modern-Irish Studies*, Vol. I, 1912-1913.

Lucas, A. T., "The Horizontal Mill in Ireland", JRSAI Vol. 83, 1953.

Mac Airt, Seán, ed/trans., *Annals of Inisfallen* (MS Rawlinson B. 503), Dublin Institute for Advanced Studies, Dublin, 1951.

Mac Néill, Eoin, *Duanaire Finn*, Vol 1, Irish Texts Society, Dublin, 1908.

Mac Niocaill, Gearóid, "Duanaire Ghearóid Iarla", *Studia Hibernica* 3, 1963, St. Patrick's Training College, Dublin.

Macalister, R.A.S., ed./trans., *Lebor Gabála Érenn*, 5 volumes, Irish Texts Society, London; 1938-56.

MacKillop, James, *A Dictionary of Celtic Mythology*, Oxford, 1998; 2000 pbk.

MacKillop, James, *Myths and Legends of the Celts*, Penguin, 2005.

MacKillop, James, *Fionn mac Cumhaill: Celtic Myth in English Literature*, Syracuse University Press, 1986, 2001.

Meyer, Kuno, *Hibernica Minora*, Oxford, 1894.

Meyer, Kuno, introduction and index by, *Rawlinson B. 502: Irish Manuscripts in the Bodleian Library*, Oxford, 1909.

Moore, Thomas, *History of Ireland*, 1846.

Murphy, Gerard, *Duanaire Finn*, Vol. II, Irish Texts Society, Dublin, 1933.

Ní Shéaghdha, Nessa, *Tóruigheacht Dhiarmada agus Ghráinne: The Pursuit of Diarmaid and Gráinne*, Irish Texts Society 48, Dublin, 1967.

Ó Dónaill, Niall, *Foclóir Gaeilge-Béarla*, Oifig an tSoláthair, Baile Átha Cliath, 1977.

Ó hÓgáin, Dáithí, *Myth, Legend and Romance: An Encyclopaedia of the Irish Folk Tradition*, Prentice Hall Press, New York, and Ryan Publishing Company, UK, 1991.

Ó hÓgáin, Dáithí, *The Lore of Ireland: An Encyclopaedia of Myth, Legend and Romance*, Collins Press, Cork, 2006.

Ó Riain, Pádraig, ed., *Cath Almaine*, Dublin Institute for Advanced Studies, 1978

O'Curry, Eugene, *Lectures on the Manuscript Materials of Ancient Irish History*, Dublin, 1873.

O'Donovan, John, ed/trans., *Annals of Ireland: Three Fragments copied from Ancient Sources by Dubhaltach Mac Firbisigh*, Irish Archaeological and Celtic Society, Dublin, 1860.

O'Donovan, John, trans., *Annals of the Kingdom of Ireland from the Earliest Times to the Year 1616*, (Annals of the Four Masters), Hodges & Smith, Dublin, 1856; De Búrca Rare Books, Dublin, 1990.

O'Grady, Standish Hayes, ed/trans., *Caithréim Thoirdhealbhaigh*, Irish Texts Society London, 1929.

O'Grady, Standish Hayes, ed., "Toruigheacht Dhiarmuda agus Grainne", *Transactions of the Ossianic Society*, Vol. 3, 1857, Dublin.

O'Grady, Standish Hayes, *Silva Gadelica*, London & Edinburgh, 1892.

O'Hanlon, John, *Lives of the Irish Saints*, Dublin, London, no date.

O'Leary, Rev. E., "Notes on the place of King Laoghaire's Death", JKAS 5, 1906-1908.

O'Rahilly, T. F., *Early Irish History and Mythology*, Dublin Institute for Advanced Studies, 1946.

O'Reilly, Joseph P., "Some Further Notes on Ancient Horizontal Water-Mills, Native and Foreign", PRIA 24, 1902-04, pp. 55 ff.

Plummer, Charles, *Lives of Irish Saints*, Vol. II, Oxford, 1922.

Price, Liam, "Historical Note on Lagore", in Hencken, op. cit.

Price, Liam, *The Place-names of Co. Wicklow*, Dublin Institute for Advanced Studies, Dublin, 1946, 1983.

Raftery, Barry, "Drumanagh and Roman Ireland", *Archaeology Ireland 35*, Vol. 10, No. 1, Spring 1996.

Rynne, Etienne, "A Togher and a Bog Road in Lullymore Bog", JKAS 14, 1964-70.

Silva Gadelica, see O'Grady, Standish Hayes.

Smyth, Alfred P., "Kings, Saints and Sagas", in Hannigan, op. cit.

Smyth, Alfred P., "The Húi Néill and the Leinstermen in the Annals of Ulster, 431-516 A. D.", *Études Celtiques*, Vol. 14, No. 1.

Smyth, Daragh, *A Guide to Irish Mythology*, Irish Academic Press, Blackrock, Co. Dublin, 1988.

Stokes, Whitley, "The Battle of Allen", *Revue Celtique* 24, 1903.

Stokes, Whitley, "The Bodleian Amra Choluimb chille", *Revue Celtique* 20, 1899. (This is the version of the 9th-century *Amra* in the 12th-century manuscript Rawlinson B. 502, source of the quatrains "Gráinne said: 'I know a man ...'" and "What you have is good, Gráinne.")

Stokes, Whitley, "The Bodleian Dinnshenchas" and "The Edinburgh Dinnshenchas", *Folk-lore* III, 1892.

Stokes, Whitley, "The Bórama", *Revue Celtique* 13, 1892.

Stokes, Whitley, "The Rennes Dindshenchas", *Revue Celtique* 15, 1894.

Stokes, Whitley, *The Birth and Life of St. Moling*, privately printed, London, 1907.

Tacitus, *Tacitus – Dialogus, Agricola, Germania*, (Agricola and Germania translated by Maurice Hutton), Heinemann (UK), Harvard (US), 1914.

Walsh, Paul, "A Story of Diarmaid Mac Cerbaill – Mullinoran and Other Place Names", *The Irish Book Lover*, Vol. 28, February 1942.

Walshe, Patrick T., "The Antiquities of the Dunlavin-Donard District", JRSAI 61, 1931.

Warner, Richard, "Tuathal Techtmar: A Myth or Ancient Literary Evidence for a Roman Invasion?", *Emania* 13, 1995.

Wood-Martin, W. G., *The Lake Dwellings of Ireland*, Hodges, Figgis, Dublin; Longmans, Green, London; 1886. Reprinted by Crannóg Editions / Beaver Row Press, Dublin, 1983.

Many of the dates in the text follow Dan McCarthy's "Chronological Synchronisation of the Irish Annals" as posted on his website:
www.cs.tcd.ie/Dan.McCarthy/chronology/synchronisms/annals-chron.htm

Printed by
Brunswick Press
Dublin